"You Will Stay, Kati. One Way or Another. . . ."

His kiss deepened, and Kati tried to fight her building passion. Finally she managed to turn her head. "No, Raul," she pleaded, her voice a quivering sigh.

"Don't fight me, Kati," he murmured. "You belong here with me in Mexico. You have the hot blood of a true Latino coursing through your veins, no matter how you wish to deny it. Only your pride makes you want to run away again."

Her skin burned where he had touched her, and she knew that he spoke the truth, but she would never admit it. "You're wrong, Raul," she managed to say.

"Kati," he said in a husky voice, "you can't lie to me. You want to stay. Admit it."

BRENDA TRENT

has a life right out of romance. She followed her heart from Virginia to California, where she met and married the man of her dreams. With his encouragement she gave up working to concentrate on another dream: writing. We are proud to present her work through Silhouette Romances.

Dear Reader:

I'd like to take this opportunity to thank you for all your support and encouragement of Silhouette Romances.

Many of you write in regularly, telling us what you like best about Silhouette, which authors are your favorites. This is a tremendous help to us as we strive to publish the best contemporary romances possible.

All the romances from Silhouette Books are for you, so enjoy this book and the many stories to come. I hope you'll continue to share your thoughts with us, and invite you to write to us at the address below:

Karen Solem
Editor-in-Chief
Silhouette Books
P.O. Box 769
New York, N.Y. 10019

BRENDA TRENT

Runaway Wife

Silhouette Romance
Published by Silhouette Books New York
America's Publisher of Contemporary Romance

Other Silhouette Books by Brenda Trent

Rising Star
Winter Dreams
A Stranger's Wife
Run from Heartache
Stormy Affair

SILHOUETTE BOOKS, a Simon & Schuster Division of
GULF & WESTERN CORPORATION
1230 Avenue of the Americas, New York, N.Y. 10020

Distributed by Pocket Books

ISBN: 0-671-57193-1

First Silhouette Books printing December, 1982

10 9 8 7 6 5 4 3 2 1

Map by Ray Lundgren

America's Publisher of Contemporary Romance

Printed in the U.S.A.

To my brother John and his wife Shirley,
and in loving memory of my brother George

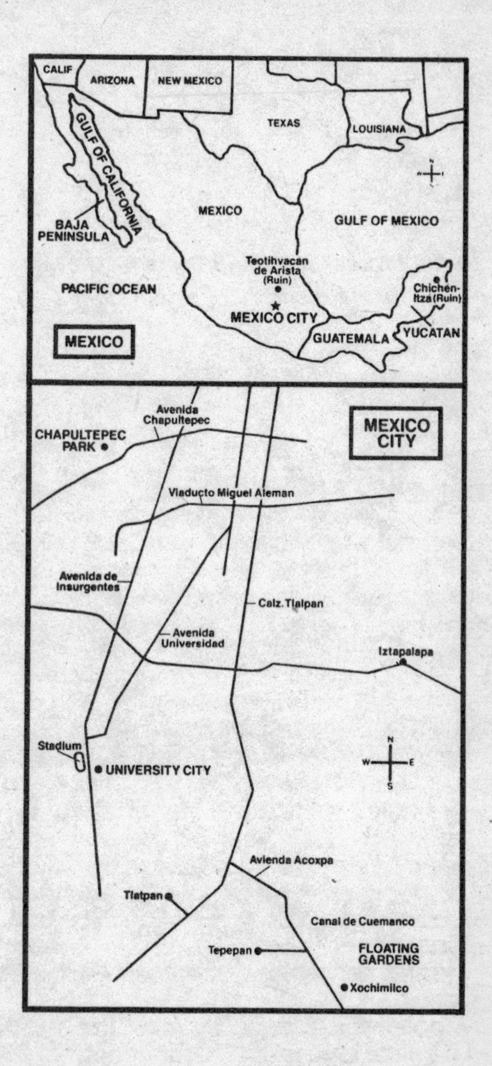
CALIF
ARIZONA
NEW MEXICO
TEXAS
LOUISIANA
GULF OF CALIFORNIA
BAJA PENINSULA
MEXICO
GULF OF MEXICO
Teotihvacan de Arista (Ruin)
Chichen-Itza (Ruin)
PACIFIC OCEAN
MEXICO CITY
MEXICO
GUATEMALA
YUCATAN
Avenida Chapultepec
CHAPULTEPEC PARK
MEXICO CITY
Viaducto Miguel Aleman
Avenida de Insurgentes
Calz. Tlalpan
Avenida Universidad
Iztapalapa
Stadium
UNIVERSITY CITY
N
W
E
S
Avienda Acoxpa
Tlatpan
Canal de Cuemanco
Tepepan
FLOATING GARDENS
Xochimilco

Chapter One

Kati stared at the line of leafy green shade trees which stood in a solemn row, baking along with everything else under a breathtakingly hot sun. Some of the trees were leaning slightly, bent by time and shaped by the wind rather than by the hand of man. Kati was pleased by the knowledge; she had seen too much of man's handiwork in the past year and not enough of nature's. The streets were quiet like the trees, and the buildings had a look of stability and permanence. It was good to be home, she mused idly, even if it was dreadfully hot. Waving a hand in front of her face to circulate the humid air of the small North Carolina town, she hurried up the steps to her apartment, the lightness in her step betraying her excitement. With one slender hand, she undid the large bow of her peach-colored blouse; with the other, she unlocked the door.

"Jenny! Jenny!" she called, her vivid green eyes sparkling as she searched the cozy living room for her roommate. "Are you home?"

A short, plump girl, dressed in snug blue shorts and a darker blue blouse, stepped into the archway of the kitchen-dining room. "In here," she called back, waving a spatula in her hand.

"Oh, you're not cooking in this weather, are you?" Kati groaned.

Jenny popped a french fry into her mouth and chewed it before she replied. "Hot or not, we still have to eat. How was your day?"

"Wonderful! Just wonderful. I finally reached that

travel agent, and she said that we can book a flight for the end of the week," Kati cried enthusiastically, unbuttoning her blouse and loosening the belt of her white pleated skirt on the way to the single bedroom. When she heard no response from Jenny, she looked back over her shoulder. "Jenny, did you hear me?"

The spatula was suspended in the air, and Jenny's pleasant features wore an apologetic look. "I'm sorry, Kati, but I can't go with you after all."

"What?" Kati cried, her eyes meeting Jenny's as she slipped off her white sandals and slid her skirt down curvy hips. "What are you saying? We've planned this trip for weeks, and I have to go now or I'll miss the fashion show."

Jenny shrugged round shoulders, a pout appearing on her pink lips. "I can't go."

"Why?"

She refused to meet Kati's eyes. "Donny was very unhappy when I told him we were going to Mexico City. You'll have to go without me."

Kati sighed in exasperation, then tossed her skirt onto a nearby chair. "Jenny, you aren't going to let that man dictate your life, are you? He certainly won't take you himself."

Jenny was instantly defensive. "At least I *have* a man," she said. Sitting down heavily on the pale green sofa, she gave an apologetic groan. "I'm sorry. I didn't mean that. I know you have your reasons, and good ones, for shying away from men, but I want to marry Donny. You know I do everything I can in anticipation of a proposal."

Kati slowly sat down by the other girl, bracing her elbows on her knees and locking her fingers together to keep them from trembling. The reasons she shied away from men could be summed up into one major one, she thought bitterly—Raul Torres, her husband. Even though they had been separated for seven months, the pain was still sharp, as if they had parted yesterday. If she lived an eternity, she would never get over the way he had hurt and humiliated her. He had shown utter disregard for her love for him. She pushed the painful memories back into the recesses of her mind. She didn't want Jenny to know how much impact her comment had had.

"And you still don't get a proposal, Jenny," she said quietly. "Has it occurred to you that you shouldn't cater to Don's every whim? Besides, it isn't unreasonable for you to take a trip without him. We've planned this since Mr. Harris told me about the fashion show. It's a wonderful opportunity for me to mix business and pleasure. Don't you want to go?"

It was an unfair question, for Jenny was plainly disappointed at the prospect of not going. Kati saw the determination that it took to force a smile onto her face when she replied, "You go without me, Kati. There's no reason for you to stay home just because I do. Your career is very important to you. Anyway, I know you've wanted to see Mexico City for years, and to have your husband take his secretary instead of you—" Jenny raised a hand to cover her mouth. "I'm sorry," she muttered forlornly. "I know I agreed never to mention that again. It just slipped out."

Lowering her eyes, Kati pretended to study the beige carpet so the other girl wouldn't see the pain she had caused. Without acknowledging the outburst, she murmured, "I don't want to go without you. Do change your mind, Jenny."

Jenny was shaking her head ruefully, but Kati saw the hesitation. "Jenny?"

Doubt filled Jenny's eyes for only a moment. Then she sighed raggedly. "I'm sorry. I know I've let you down. I know your obsession with . . . with Mexico, but I just can't go now."

Kati ignored the innuendo. She had wanted to go to Mexico long before she ever met Raul Torres. When she was a teenager, an uncle had brought her a painting from Acapulco done on thin bark. She was so fascinated with it that she had read everything she could on

Mexican crafts. She had become enchanted with the country, and she treasured the painting above all else. Inadvertently, it had been sold along with the other household goods when her parents had died two years ago. The huge old mansion she had lived in all her life had been too lonely. Haunted by the memories of her parents, Kati finally gave up the house and all the furniture to move in with her childhood friend, Jenny. Still, she couldn't deny that Raul's description of Mexico City had made it so appealing that she had promised herself she would see it. The fashion show was only an added incentive. Mr. Harris had met the famous Mexican designer, Paco Cueto, when he attended a fashion convention in New York, and he knew that Paco was having a special show created around native costumes which Kati was sure to find fascinating. She herself worked her designs around the colonial gowns of the South. She did want to go rather badly.

"Well, maybe one of the other girls can go," she murmured thoughtfully.

"No!" Jenny insisted quickly, causing Kati to look at her curiously. "I mean just about every single one of them has already planned her vacation," Jenny clarified. "You know how Mr. Harris is about planning time off."

Kati nodded. She and Jenny worked for the same clothing manufacturer, and she did know how inflexible Mr. Harris could be. She pursed her lips, then reached over to pick up her skirt. "It really doesn't matter. It was all a dream anyway."

Jenny stood up. "Go alone, Kati. You must go. There will be other people to make friends with. I'm sure you'll have a wonderful time. The agency rep said you can arrange a different tour every single day right there in the hotel. You'll meet other people. Don't put the trip off another year. Besides, you never know who you'll meet in Mexico City. After all," she added slyly, "you do have friends there."

Kati rolled her eyes at the other girl. "I know you're

referring to Raul, Jenny, and he can hardly be classified as a friend."

"Lover?" Jenny retorted, her blue eyes twinkling mischievously, a smile playing on her lips.

A vision of a tall, dark man surfaced, his face arrogant and cold. Kati quickly forced it into the back of her mind. It was agony to remember how intensely she had loved him. "That's not funny," she said. Strolling to the bedroom, she pulled shorts and a halter from the chest of drawers before she slipped off her blouse. "Anyway," she said, finding it hard to keep Raul out of her thoughts, "I wouldn't go to Mexico City if I had the faintest notion that Raul would be there. He never goes in the summer. He's obsessed with his business."

Even the mention of his name evoked painful, half-buried memories. Kati had refused to think about what a fool Raul had made of her. Carefully concealing what he had done from everyone but Jenny, she had returned to her Southern home, finding comfort and refuge in the familiar, stable surroundings. The frivolity of New York had paled for her as quickly as Raul's love. Hoping Jenny couldn't see the slight tremble of her hand, Kati slid the red terrycloth shorts up her shapely legs, then took off her bra and tugged the clinging red and white halter top into place over her generous breasts. "Do you think this is too daring?" she asked to change the subject.

"No, but I think you should be outlawed, Kati," Jenny replied admiringly as she lingered in the doorway. "Oh, if only I had that figure, Donny would have proposed to me months ago."

"How about this nose?" Kati asked, tracing the slight rise in the bridge with her fingertip. Though she didn't really dislike it, she felt that it kept her from being pretty.

"Nope! Only the figure," Jenny said teasingly. Her own nose was small and pert. "However, I've never known anyone to object to your nose. Oh, do go to

Mexico City. I know you'll kick yourself if you miss that show when you've been wanting to go so badly. And you'll meet some new friends in no time, not to mention an assortment of suitors."

"I don't want suitors," Kati replied impatiently.

"You can't confine your social life to a few dinner dates with good ol' safe Henry Bowden. You can't swear off men forever because of one unhappy experience," Jenny insisted with sudden sobriety. "You're much too young and much too pretty. At twenty-three, your life has just begun."

Kati had known Henry since high school; she did date him because theirs was a comfortable, platonic relationship, but she didn't want to tell Jenny that. "I enjoy Henry's company," she replied. "And besides, listen to you," she teased. "You're all of twenty-four."

"And never been married," Jenny cried woefully.

"Consider yourself lucky." Kati couldn't keep the bitterness out of her voice as she strolled barefoot back into the living room, Jenny trailing behind. Kati went over to the corner where her drawing board was set up and stood scrutinizing the frilly party dress she had been sketching for several days. She picked up her pencil and added a few pleats to the skirt, then erased them immediately. She was too upset to work on the dress. Laying the pencil down, she began to make a single braid of the masses of straight, black hair that tumbled about her shoulders. "I wish Mr. Moffet would turn up the air conditioning a single degree. Anything. I want to conserve energy, too, but it's stifling in here." Suddenly she sniffed smoky air. "Jenny!" she cried. "You cook as badly as I do!" Running on small feet, she reached the kitchen just in time to drag a smoldering pan off the stove. "Well," she said good-naturedly, "that was dinner. Now, why don't we grab a hamburger down at the corner?"

Jenny wrinkled her nose at the burned pan and the ruined steaks. "I've never done that before." Her eyes met Kati's in a mock plea. "Can't we afford more than a hamburger? After all, you're an up-and-coming dress designer."

Kati smiled at the description of her career. "I should have stayed with Martin's. There I might eventually have been up-and-coming, but I only lasted four weeks. Even then you know I hadn't done any real designing. Mr. Martin firmly believed that a designer had to learn every other area of dressmaking first by actually working at the business. I was just starting pattern making."

She laughed lightly as she remembered the big dreams she'd had when she went to New York's fashionable Seventh Avenue in search of a house that would appreciate her sketches. She had been so naive. She was fortunate that Mr. Martin had hired her as an apprentice designer . . . she couldn't even be called an assistant. He allowed her to present her designs, and she had done so, but with little effect. She had stubbornly clung to a dream of elegance from an earlier time; studying the beautiful colonial gowns of the South, she had used them as a basis for her modern dresses. She believed in her work, and she knew that someone would appreciate it at some time, but she hadn't been prepared for the pushy, competitive atmosphere of New York.

"Now," she continued thoughtfully, "you know that I do more sewing than designing since Mr. Harris doesn't have a budget that includes designers. That one design of mine he used is selling well, though. The other three which were bought for originals netted a tidy little sum. And that, my friend, is the extent of my mark in the fashion world."

Jenny giggled. "That's what happens when you let a man take precedence over a career. Now you're back at square one."

Holding up a warning hand, Kati murmured, "Don't remind me again. I'm trying to forget." After her experiences with Raul and New York, she had run back to North Carolina to the security of home and friends like a frightened rabbit. Only her dress designing had enabled her to keep her sanity at the time. She didn't want to dwell on Raul now.

"Please go to Mexico City," Jenny said fervently, and Kati turned to look at her curiously.

"Why do you keep saying that?" Her large green eyes were puzzled. Going alone certainly didn't sound appealing no matter how wildly she wanted to go, and she had never known Jenny to be so insistent.

"You'll meet someone to share the experience with. I know you will, and I don't want to see your dreams shattered because of me. You know this is a chance for you to see how a famous designer works his designs around old costumes just as you do." She smiled hesitantly. "If you keep waiting for people like me to go along, who knows when you'll ever get there."

Kati thought it odd that Jenny should promote the trip so ardently now that she wasn't going. For a moment she wondered if her old friend wanted to be rid of her. "Jenny, are you planning something in my absence?" she asked as her exquisitely arched brows met in a frown. She was surprised by the flush that raced up Jenny's cheeks.

"No," her friend replied quickly. "No, of course not. It's just that I don't want to see you unhappy, Kati. Won't you take the trip?"

Kati looked thoughtful for a moment. Perhaps there was something in what Jenny was saying. Why should she wait and dream and plan around someone else? She had done that twice now, and both times had been a big disappointment. She couldn't base her career on the whims of others. She shrugged as she looked at her roommate. "Why not?"

Jenny stepped closer to hug Kati tightly. "You won't be sorry! Oh, I know you won't!"

Holding her friend at arm's length, Kati asked suspiciously, "How do you know?"

Jenny averted her eyes and shrugged lightly. "How can you be sorry when it sounds like such a wonderful trip?"

"Jenny," Kati persisted uncomfortably, "are you sure you're not up to something?"

Innocent blue eyes met Kati's vivid green ones. "What could I possibly be up to?"

Kati didn't know, and it was apparent that she wasn't going to learn. "Oh, come on, let's go eat."

"You really won't be sorry," Jenny repeated, but this time Kati ignored the comment. She would go to Mexico and find out for herself if she were sorry or not.

Kati was more than a little apprehensive when she stepped down from the plane with the other Mexico City passengers and filed into the busy airport. Smoothing down her green-flowered sundress, she looked around for the baggage pickup. She located it at last, only to find that she couldn't reach her suitcase through the crowd of people who were lined two deep, forming an impenetrable wall between herself and the luggage. When the suitcase had gone around on the revolving belt twice, she asked a tall stranger to grab it for her. After thanking the blond man with a smile, she milled around aimlessly for several minutes, reading signs and trying to decide what to do. She had never been out of the country before, and she felt terribly lost. Finally she got in a long line of people whose papers were being checked by a pretty Mexican girl. Nervously, she pulled out her tourist visa and looked it over.

"You didn't sign the back."

Startled by the voice behind her, she turned around and gazed into the eyes of the blond man who had helped her with her suitcase. He was in his twenties, but his curly hair and boyish grin made him appear younger. "You have to sign the back," he said, smiling warmly at her and pointing to his name on the form.

"Thank you, Darren Davies." Kati read the bold, clear handwriting easily. Awkwardly resting the form on her purse, made bulky by her folder of sketches poking out the top, she signed in the appropriate place.

As she wrote Kati Autumn, she remembered the objections Tandy Talbert, the travel agent, had made, insisting that Kati use her married name because it was her legal one. But Kati had refused. She had consulted a lawyer when she left Raul, and he had assured her that it was quite legal to use her maiden name; after all, some women didn't bother to take their husbands' names at all these days. Looking around the room restlessly, she waited her turn to pass through the customs turnstile. When she was inside the next room, she paused in confusion, then glanced back at Darren and smiled. She didn't want anyone to know that she had been in the country ten minutes and she was lost already.

"Can I help you with anything?" he asked, his tone pleasant.

"I'm afraid I'm at a loss as to what to do," she murmured in embarrassment. "I'm booked at the Hotel . . ." Before she could complete her statement, a nice-looking man of medium height with warm brown eyes approached her.

"Kati Torres?" he asked in slightly accented English.

"Autumn," she corrected quickly. She hadn't used her married name since she left Raul seven months ago, and she had no idea how this man knew it. Tandy! she thought suddenly. Darn that woman! She had used Torres anyway.

He gave no indication of surprise. "Kati Autumn," he said as if she hadn't corrected him at all, "I'm José Adriano. I'm here to drive you to your hotel."

She looked at him hesitantly for a moment, unsure if she should go with him. She didn't know if someone were scheduled to meet her, or if she were responsible for getting her own transportation.

"It's okay," he assured her, his smile revealing strong, white teeth. "You were booked into the Hotel Esteben by Miss Tandy Talbert, the travel agent, were you not?"

Kati smiled. "Yes, I was. Did she send you?"

"Right this way." He took her arm, gently guiding her to a waiting black car.

She glanced back over her shoulder. "Perhaps I'll see you around town, Darren."

"Just a moment," he called, hurrying to her side, his luggage in hand. "Excuse me, you said the Hotel Esteben. I'm booked there. May I have a ride?"

José's warm brown eyes cooled visibly. "I'm sorry, sir," he murmured. "This is a private car."

While Kati raised puzzled brows, José, ignoring Darren, opened the car door and ushered her in. Shrugging helplessly, she peered out the window at an exasperated Darren. She watched him until her attention was attracted by the surging traffic. She gasped as José barely missed a red automobile, then honked his horn several times, the blast sounding loudly in Kati's ears.

His eyes met hers in the rearview mirror and he recognized her alarm. "It's okay," he said. "There are about two and a half million cars in this city. Considering that there are so many, we have few accidents, but I caution you to be careful if you are a pedestrian. A pedestrian must run for his life when he steps out on the street!"

Kati acknowledged the information with a nod of her head. She would be careful all right. Even in the protection of the car, she was frightened by the heavy traffic; the drivers seemed to stop, start and merge at will, oblivious to traffic regulations. They obviously took delight in tooting their horns; they all did it frequently and at the slightest provocation.

Kati didn't loosen her grip on her seat until José parked the car in front of a graceful, old hotel on Reforma Avenue. Walking around to the rear of the car, he opened the door and helped her out. When he had escorted her into the hotel lobby, she glanced around at her surroundings and felt at home immediately. The hotel lobby reflected the elegant splendor of a time past. Red circular seats curved restfully before large windows; stone lions rested on their paws, unmindful of the numerous visitors bustling about; bellboys dressed in sleek black trousers and stiff white shirts waited with eager smiles to do the guests' bidding, and two ancient glass-doored elevators chimed loudly as they carried carloads of people up eleven floors and down again.

Kati approached the desk hesitantly, uncertain if she would need her rusty Spanish to confirm her reservation and to sign the guest register. To her surprise, José spoke rapidly to the clerk, and the man turned to survey her. A broad smile creased his face and he appraised her figure and face quickly before answering in the same rapid-fire manner. Kati tried her best to understand the exchange, but the most she could translate were half a dozen words, and they made no sense to her. José seemed to have mentioned Raul Torres, but that was ridiculous. He must have given Kati's name, using Torres for the surname. Kati thought the clerk replied that she was a pretty bride, which was absurd. She sighed and gave up trying to decipher the volley of words; she certainly hoped the other people she spoke with didn't talk as fast as these two or her scant knowledge of the language would be little better than useless.

José turned to her with twinkling brown eyes. "This is Miguel, Señora . . . *perdóneme,* Señorita Kati Autumn."

Kati was sure Miguel and José exchanged conspiratorial smiles, but she couldn't see anything amusing in her name or her status. "I'm pleased to meet you, Miguel," she said stiffly. She was tired, and she suddenly realized that she had chosen the wrong season to visit Mexico City. It hadn't dawned on her until now, but the lobby didn't appear to be air-conditioned, and she was quite warm. "I'd like to register and go to my room if I may," she said in precise English.

To her surprise, Miguel replied in English, "Yes, of course. Please sign here." He turned the register so she could write her name, then tapped a gold bell. Immediately a boy arrived at her side and took her luggage in hand.

"This way," he said in a heavy accent, and Kati gladly followed him. Only at the last minute did she remember to turn and thank José. Her face turned scarlet when her eyes met his. He had been watching her, his dark brown eyes traveling slowly up her body; he seemed almost as embarrassed as she that he had been caught in the act of observing her so carefully.

"Thank you for the ride," she mumbled quickly, then hurriedly stepped into the crowded, waiting elevator.

After tipping the bellboy, she looked around her hotel room. It had ambiance. The walls were a mellow yellow, the carpet gold and red flowered; a bright yellow bedspread flowed to the floor from the large bed on the left side of the room. A round hardwood table and two gold chairs were beside it. A large Spanish-style bureau completed the furnishings. Kati briefly explored a walk-in closet and the yellow-tiled bathroom with its free-standing old-fashioned sink. A large, gilt-edged mirror dominated one wall alongside an ornate water closet, and Kati smiled at the charm of the antique fixtures. Thinking a bath would be just the thing to perk her up, she undressed, twisted her hair up on top of her head, and climbed into a claw-footed tub full of tepid water.

When she had bathed and relaxed a bit, she dried on a yellow towel. With the towel wrapped around her, one corner tucked securely, she placed her suitcase on the bed and unpacked it, leaving out a salmon-colored voile dress to wear to dinner. She would eat and return to her room to get a good night's rest; tomorrow she wanted to start the tours of the city, and she had been told that the bus left the hotel at nine.

She was pleased by the fancy, intimate tables with dusky rose cloths and delicate place settings when she walked into the dining room. On each table was a red carnation and a white candle. Kati smiled at the irony of being alone in such a romantic setting.

A tall, thin maitre d' greeted her first in Spanish, then in English, and escorted her to a somewhat isolated table. She settled into the chair the man had pulled out for her. Then she accepted a long menu and sat studying it.

She was still trying to decide on a dish when a man appeared at the table. Not looking up, Kati murmured, "I'm not ready to order yet." Her eyes raced down the menu again. The problem was that it was in Spanish. She raised her eyes to ask if there were an English equivalent, and a gasp escaped her softly parted lips. Her heart suddenly began to beat as though a hundred horses thundered through it. The man standing at her side was her husband of ten months, Raul Torres!

"What are you doing here?" she cried, dropping her linen napkin to the floor as she attempted to stand. A firm hand pressed her back down onto the chair as midnight black brows arched up tauntingly.

"Please don't get up, Kati. I'll join you for dinner," he said smoothly, as if he were an old friend she had met unexpectedly.

"No!" she cried, jumping up before he could restrain her again. Her only thought was to get as far away from this powerful, dark man as she could.

Raul grasped her firmly by her wrist and whirled her back toward him. Before Kati could protest, his arms wound around her in a steel grip and he hugged her to his hard chest, his warm lips whispering in her ear, "You're making a terrible scene, Kati. Everyone is looking at you."

Involuntarily, Kati's gaze darted around the room, and she saw that what Raul said was true. They were the center of attention; other diners had paused in their eating and conversation to watch Raul and Kati in their isolated corner. The sight had a somewhat mollifying effect on Kati's panic and, still captive in his arms, she tilted her head back to look up into his ebony eyes. She knew from past experience that Raul was very conscious of what he considered to be acceptable standards of behavior; making a scene in public was not one of them.

"Now," he said in a low, calm voice, "if you'll sit down, we can have dinner."

Face flaming, heart pounding, Kati seated herself again. Instead of sitting across from her, Raul moved his chair close by hers.

"I don't want you to join me," Kati hissed. She was acutely aware that she was near tears. Seeing Raul after all these months had been a dreadful shock. She had tried so hard to forget all about him, and she hadn't thought about him any more than she could help. She drew a deep breath. "How did you know I was here? What do you want?"

A slow smile spread over his generous lips. "Such questions, *querida*. I'm your husband."

Brilliant green eyes met his glittering black ones. "Don't play games with me. How did you know I was here?"

He took one of her hands and lifted it to his soft lips before Kati could snatch it away. "Jenny," he said simply. "Jenny is my friend as well as yours." He laughed softly and dangerously. "Unlike you, she appreciates a handsome man."

"You're despicable!" Kati cried. "So arrogant and sure of yourself."

Raul laughed again. "Don't you find me handsome, Kati?"

"No!" she spat, but it was a lie. Raul Torres was the most handsome man she had ever seen in her life, and she was sure she would never meet his equal. His bearing was commanding and majestic, and he was always as impeccably dressed as he was now. Her eyes skimmed over the expensive, immaculate white linen suit and the deep maroon of his shirt, and she tried not to stare at the dark hairs curling over the edge of the sleek material. She met Raul's eyes again, but she found her own straying helplessly to the aristocratic nose, the full cupid's bow lips, the arrogant thrust of the strong chin and chiseled jaw.

"No?" he taunted softly, and she realized that he had watched her scrutinizing him.

"How unfortunate then that you will spend a lifetime tied to me, *querida,*" he murmured, his eyes dancing with golden highlights, his lips parting to expose even, white teeth.

"I won't spend a single day with you, señor!" she cried. She sucked in her breath sharply. How dared Jenny be a party to this deception? Don hadn't forbidden her to come at all; Jenny had sacrificed her trip so that Raul could be here instead. Angry tears stung Kati's eyes at her friend's betrayal; Jenny knew better than anyone in the world how deeply Raul had wounded her. Why had she done this?

"Jenny had no right to tell you I was coming!" she cried. "She didn't tell me anything about being in touch with you."

"Don't be too harsh on Jenny. I called her to inquire about you, and she happened to mention that you wanted to vacation here. I persuaded Jenny to convince you to come alone."

"Why?"

"Because I wanted to see you. Don't tell me you didn't even intend to contact me while you were in my city." His tone was teasing, and it irritated Kati terribly.

"I did not!" she declared. "I didn't even think you would be here now. Isn't this the busy time for your business?"

"My father is ill," Raul replied solemnly.

"I'm sorry," Kati murmured. "I hope it isn't serious."

"I'm afraid it is," he said. "It has lasted for some time."

Kati looked away. She didn't even know his father and she didn't want to feel sorry for him or Raul.

"Kati, would you have come to Mexico to have fun without even a thought of me?" he asked gently.

Kati was glad he had changed the subject, even though she knew he was making reference to the many plans they had made to see Mexico together. "Yes," she retorted. "Anyway, I'm here for business as well as pleasure." She smiled a little triumphantly. "My designs are doing quite well, and I'm not even working as a designer." Raul had never been interested in her career. "I'm here to see a show done by Paco Cueto. My boss, Mr. Harris, feels it will be beneficial for me since I work with old costume designs, too."

"Oh?" Raul's brows arched up, and Kati smugly observed that he was surprised that her designs were doing so well. "I know Paco Cueto," he said. "He is a friend of mine and my father's."

"Oh," Kati murmured with a hint of disappointment. She would have preferred that Raul didn't know the designer.

"Will you have wine with dinner, Señor Torres?"

Kati looked away as the waiter, speaking flawless English, stepped up to the table. She suddenly wondered if the entire hotel had been a party to Raul's treachery. Obviously José had been sent by Raul, and she had been right in thinking the clerk and José were discussing her as Raul's wife. It had been a big, big mistake to come to her husband's hometown, regardless of how often she had dreamed of the trip.

"Shall we have white wine, Kati?" Raul asked.

She shook her head. "I'm not thirsty."

His lips formed a half-smile. "The wine will do you good." Turning to the waiter, he said, "The house wine, please, for two."

Kati's eyes blazed at him, but she waited until the waiter had gone to speak. "I don't want wine, I don't want dinner, and I don't want your company. I don't know why you're here, and I don't care. Now if you'll excuse me." She rose abruptly and started from the table, but Raul grasped her hand before she could escape.

Gently stroking the soft skin with his thumb, he spoke quietly. "Kati, stay and have dinner with me. I want to talk to you. That's all I ask. I am your husband, and it shouldn't be too much to request that you spend a single hour with me." There was no pleading in his eyes or in his tone. Raul Torres didn't beg anyone, least of all his estranged wife, and Kati suddenly had a fierce desire to see him humbled . . . just once.

She looked away from him, her eyes sweeping around the room, not caring that she was still the object of a few curious stares. Raul's thumb continued its sensuous movement against her skin, and Kati tried to ignore the sensations that the single action was creating within her.

"One hour, Kati. What can it cost you? You're already here, and you would have eaten at this time anyway."

Kati sighed wearily, knowing as she sat back down that she was making a dreadful mistake. One hour with Raul was like a lifetime, and it would take her years to forget it. Her pride had been shattered when she found out that Raul preferred another woman, and she wanted so much to despise him. "What do you want of me?" she asked, feeling a tightening in her throat.

He smiled as though there was no dissension between them. "All of you," he said suggestively. His dark eyes probed hers. "But since you seem . . . ah . . . momentarily unwilling to give of yourself, I'll settle for an hour."

She shook her head, angry that he was toying with her. "What do you hope to prove by meeting me here?"

"That you love me."

Kati sucked in her breath. "I don't love you! I left you because I don't love you!"

For the first time since he had joined her, Raul's

beautiful lips ceased to smile as they narrowed into a grim line. As she had seen so many times before, Kati saw the arrogant line of his strong chin. "I don't believe you, *querida,"* he stated flatly. She realized she had wounded his pride, and she was glad. "You're behaving foolishly," he said sharply. "You've acted like a spoiled, selfish child."

"Don't talk to me like that," she hissed raggedly. He had some nerve after the way he had treated her.

"Then tell me why you ran back home to North Carolina after three months of marriage."

Kati lifted her chin and her eyes met his. Of course she wouldn't speak to him of the shame and the heartache he had caused her. He knew as well as she did why she had left him, and she refused to humiliate herself further by letting him hear it from her own lips. Closing her mouth resolutely, she looked away from him. She would *never* give him the satisfaction of hearing her tell him.

Chapter Two

Kati was relieved when the waiter returned with a bottle of wine in a fancy silver ice bucket. Uncorking the bottle, he poured a small amount into Raul's glass. He sipped it, then complimented the waiter on its taste. Kati sat with her hands clenched into fists while the waiter poured for her. Then she gripped her glass tightly, her knuckles white as she lifted it to her lips to swallow a considerable amount. If she didn't manage to relax somehow, she would never be able to endure this hour. What a dreadful nightmare her beautiful dream was turning into. Never had she imagined that Raul would be in town now. His import-export business on New York's Seventh Avenue was usually booming in the sweltering heat of summer.

When the waiter left, Raul smoothly returned to his subject. "Jealousy is no reason to break up a marriage, Kati," he commented blandly, as though she had used very bad taste in committing such an act. "And don't deny that jealousy was the culprit."

Kati would die before she would let Raul know how cruelly she felt the barb of his words. Jealousy indeed! Did he take her for a complete fool? He had married her, made love to her, set her up in his New York penthouse, then returned to Mexico to his family home with his mistress in the guise of his secretary! Kati had never even met his parents—father, she corrected, for she knew that the elder Señor Torres was all the immediate family Raul had. She had wondered a million times if Raul had even told his father that he had married.

She smiled bitterly at the memory of that day last Christmas when she had told Raul of her plans to purchase the biggest live Scotch pine she could find and invite their friends to help them decorate it. She had said it to please him, for really she would have preferred only the two of them. He had announced that he would be in Mexico City on Christmas day. Like a fool, Kati had thought she would go with him. But she had thought wrong. Brisa Mendoza had gone with him, had spent Christmas day with him, had dined with his father—not Kati, his American wife of three months.

The bitter smile was fixed on Kati's lips as she thought about Raul blaming their breakup on her jealousy. He had often accused her of being jealous; she had lost count of the times they had quarrelled over Raul calling Brisa sweet names and paying undue attention to her. Brisa was his personal secretary, and he openly flirted with her, deliberately to torment Kati, it seemed. Raul had once told her that Brisa was his cousin, but Kati wasn't naive enough to believe it. She had scoffed at him, and it had only served to make him more bold with his attentions to the other girl. Kati had seethed with jealousy.

But that kind of jealousy she could at least endure. Taking Brisa to Mexico was a different matter altogether. Kati had been cruelly disappointed when he told her that he couldn't take her with him for reasons he didn't want to get into at the time, but she had accepted it quietly. Then she had called his home number in Mexico City the night of his flight, Christmas Eve, eager to hear his voice, to know that he had arrived safely. And Brisa had answered. Kati would have known that sugary voice anywhere; she had heard it too many times when she had called Raul at the office. She had been shocked, but she had quietly asked that Raul return the call. She had waited all that night and all the next day, but he had never called.

"Kati."

The bitter smile died on her lips as she faced her husband. She glared at him but said nothing.

"What were you smiling at, *querida?*"

"Stop calling me that," she demanded. "Save your sweet words for Brisa. Is she here with you?"

His eyes mocked her, but the waiter returned to take their order before he could reply. Kati looked at the items on the menu with distaste. Raul had worked feverishly in those three months to teach her basic Spanish, but he had always been with her when they had ordered Mexican food, and she hadn't bothered to learn the names of the different dishes other than the more common tacos, tostadas and enchiladas. And even with those few words, he had teased her about speaking Spanish with a Southern accent.

"What will you have?" he asked, watching her with dark eyes.

"Your taste is exquisite . . . in food," she said sarcastically, not wanting him to know that she couldn't tell one dish from the other. "You can order for me."

He laughed and Kati knew it was at her condescending tone. It had always amused him to see her behave with a hauteur which she had to pretend. It came so naturally to Raul. Even though their marriage had lasted only three months and their courtship a considerably shorter time, their union had been one of ice and fire, and they had seen each other at their most serene and at their most volatile.

Raul looked up at the waiter as he placed two orders for *pipían verde de pepita.* When the waiter nodded and moved away, Raul's eyes found Kati's again.

"How long will you be staying?"

She glowered at him. "I had intended to stay two weeks, but I've changed my mind. I'll be taking the next plane out of here."

His smile was broad. "That won't be easy. You must confirm an international flight at least twenty-four hours in advance, preferably thirty-six, not to mention booking one."

Kati frowned. She hadn't known anything about the necessity of confirming so far in advance. She ruefully remembered how busy her agent had been when she spoke with her, and she vowed to give the woman a piece of her mind for the lack of information when she got home. "Well, then," she said, trying to look unperturbed, "I'll take the first available flight."

Raul took a sip of his wine, then set his glass down. His lean hand reached out and found Kati's as she fiddled nervously with her silverware. "Stay the two weeks, Kati. Don't ruin this time for yourself. Stay and let me show you the sights of Mexico City. It's a beautiful and fascinating city, and I know you've always wanted to explore it." His voice grew deceptively soft. "We talked about it so often, remember? I had always planned to be the one to introduce it to you." His eyes studied her face. "I *will* show it to you as I had planned."

Kati shook her head in denial, but his soft tone caused little shivers to race up her spine. Yes, she remembered how often they had talked of it. Raul had told her of the city's most romantic settings, and he had elaborated on the beauty of his home. He had whispered that they would make love in a bedroom where Spanish conquistadors had slept. Then Raul had taken Brisa home to Mexico City with him that Christmas last year. Had she made love with him in that same room? Kati wondered bitterly as she lowered her dark lashes to conceal forming tears. Brisa! A picture of the Mexican girl flashed in her mind: a dark beauty with rich brown hair that matched the color of her striking eyes. A dramatic, proud, slender figure—so haughty, so arrogant. She and Raul could have been made for each other.

Raul didn't comment on Kati's refusal to allow him to squire her about the city. He smiled mockingly at her, then fell silent, studying her with an unreadable expression as they waited for the meal. Kati watched other diners enter the room, noting each detail of their attire with a practiced eye for fashion, grateful for a distraction until a fresh fruit salad arrived. Her appetite had vanished entirely but she picked at the bright slices of papaya and watermelon, taking little pleasure in their sweetness. She watched idly as Raul sprinkled lime juice over his papaya, and she wondered if this was customary.

"We'll get an early start tomorrow," he announced matter-of-factly. "I have many interesting places to show you. They will take up all your time here. There will be no need to make additional plans."

"I'll not allow you to organize my vacation! Who do you think you are?" Kati demanded.

Raul straightened, pride evident in every line of his magnificent body. "I know who I am," he stated coolly. "My heritage dates all the way back to the Aztecs who were conquered by the Spaniards. My people, like my city, have only grown stronger by the trials and the tribulations of conquerors, rulers, revolutions and changing times. I am Raul Francisco Torres. Yes, I know who I am. And I know what I want. And I have *always* gotten it, *querida.*"

Kati's chin lifted in challenge. She wanted to tell him that if he were referring to her, he would fail to get what he wanted for the first time in his life. But she didn't say anything; it would be too humiliating if he said he didn't want her. And, after all, he hadn't said he did—only that he wanted to show her Mexico City. She knew the tremendous pride he took in it, and she wondered for a moment if his intentions toward her stopped at that point. Was she being vain and silly? Was it only his fierce pride that had sent him here to meet her in order to keep his word about showing her his city? She felt a flush of red race up to her face at the thought.

The joke would be on her if he wanted nothing more

than that. Here she was thinking that he intended to revive their marriage, that he wanted her as his wife again. How could she jump to such a ridiculous conclusion? He hadn't tried to contact her at all other than a single bitter phone call when he had returned to his penthouse and found her missing. He had met Jenny on two occasions, and he had tracked Kati to her apartment. She smiled to herself. What a silly little fool she was to sit here and imagine that his appearance was significant. After all, he had Brisa. Again she wondered if the girl were in Mexico now, but she would not ask again.

The food was served, and Kati ate the delicious chicken in green pumpkin seed sauce with more enthusiasm than she had shown toward the fruit. For the first time since Raul had come to the table, she entertained the idea of staying the full two weeks. Why should she let Raul spoil her dream? After the novelty of seeing her tonight, he probably wouldn't persist in his attentions to her if she were firm with him. If he hadn't pursued a runaway wife in the seven months of their separation, why should he be adamant now?

"Is the dish to your satisfaction?" he asked, drawing her attention away from her reflections.

"Yes, it's very good," she replied, looking up at him from beneath her thick lashes. And yet, she mused, it was dangerous to have any contact with Raul. As her panic and confusion subsided, she felt memories and old hurts take their place. She had loved Raul too deeply, too quickly. He had swept her off her feet with his smooth ways and his polished manners. The son of a Mexican father and an American mother, Raul had met Kati when she went to New York to show some of her dress designs to Mr. Martin of Martin Glamorette. Raul and Mr. Martin, whose businesses were less than a block apart, occasionally lunched together. Raul always stopped by to pick up Mr. Martin, and he had made it plain that he found Kati attractive when he first saw her.

The trip to New York had been Kati's first alone, and she had felt insecure and lost in such an impersonal city. She had been nervous and shy when Raul approached her, but she had been so consumed by his magnetism and charm that, foolishly, she had agreed to marry him nine days after they met. Of course, it had been a mistake of tremendous magnitude. She hadn't known him at all: how proud and disdainful he was, how he expected her to conform to his wishes, how he would openly flirt with other women, then confuse Kati with soft Spanish phrases when she objected to his cavalier behavior. That the marriage had endured three months was amazing. Three months of fire, flame, anger, ice, ecstasy and disappointment. He had insisted that she give up her budding career and stay home to raise children. And he had added insult to injury with Brisa. Kati had run away in shame, pain, and humiliation while he was still in Mexico City.

Kati was startled when he spoke again. Apparently, he had decided to direct the conversation into safer channels and he made polite chitchat, asking her about the weather in North Carolina.

Taking another long sip of her wine, Kati relaxed the slightest bit. "It's hot there," she said lightly. "But it's hot here too, although I haven't seen the sun. Where is the sunshine Mexico is famous for? All I've seen are clouds."

He smiled lazily. "You've come in the rainy season. Didn't you know? We've been suffering a long drought, but it looks like rain at last."

"The rainy season!" she cried. "No, I didn't know. My travel agent told me to bring a bathing suit."

"Yes. For walking in the rain," he teased, his eyes dancing mischievously.

"Oh, that woman!" Kati cried. "She needs to take the trip herself. I honestly don't think she knows much about Mexico at all."

Raul grinned in that reckless way of his, and Kati felt

her heartbeat increase. "Perhaps I should give the agent a tour of the city," he murmured suggestively.

"Perhaps you should," Kati retorted hostilely. *"She* might appreciate it!"

Raul laughed aloud, the sound deep and throaty, and Kati remembered a thousand other times she had thrilled to that laughter. She had already spent as much time with him as her heart could stand this evening. She got up abruptly. "I don't care for dessert, but thank you for the dinner." She extended a slender hand and Raul grasped it in his, rising as he did so. Pulling a bill from his shirt pocket, he tossed it carelessly on the table. "I'll see you to your room."

"That won't be necessary."

"I insist," he murmured, guiding her from the restaurant, a firm hand on her elbow.

Kati opened her mouth to protest, but she knew it would be useless. She was sure he knew which room she was in anyway, and she might as well go along with him. Tomorrow she would be in control of the situation; she would get up early and take the bus tour of the city. Only tonight would she let him have his way.

She wasn't prepared for just how much of her time Raul intended to take. She didn't give her room number, but he went directly to it, confirming her suspicions that he had known it already. When she pulled the key from her purse, he took it to unlock the door. Kati stepped away from him, intoxicated by his magnetic nearness. She could detect the faint but distinct smell of his after-shave, and she wondered if he had shaved just for her. She knew his beard was heavy, and by evening there were usually traces of black stubble on his chin. Her eyes searched for a hint of that darkness, but his firm jaw was clean-shaven and much too appealing. She had a sudden longing to trace the hard line with her fingertip.

She stepped inside quickly when he opened the door. "Good night," she said firmly.

Raul thrust the door open and sauntered into the room as if he owned it. With an almost indiscernible motion of his foot, he nudged the door closed and moved toward Kati.

"No," she cried, recognizing his intention, but he was heedless to her cry. With a hand of steel, he dragged her to him, gathering her to his hard length as his well-defined lips descended to claim hers in a demanding, possessive kiss. Kati struggled, feeling her breasts tingle where they were crushed against his broad chest. She tried to turn her head away, but he restricted her movements. His lips continued to press against hers warmly, and she felt them forced apart by his probing, moist tongue. A shiver slipped through her as he slowly seduced her, his hips mating with hers as he backed her against the door, ensuring her inability to escape. She had prepared for this moment so often in her dreams, but she couldn't give in now. A thousand times, she had imagined that he would come to her again, begging her to forgive him, explaining away all the ugliness and heartache caused by Brisa. But he hadn't apologized at all.

A soft moan rose in her throat, and she held her body rigid, determined that Raul wouldn't have the devastating effect on her that he had once had. She concentrated on all the misery and heartache he had caused her, but it was to no avail. Raul did not relent, and Kati's body was his ally. She felt the hatred and the bitterness drain from her like sand from an hourglass; a burning excitement and hungry passion rose to take its place. She had waited so long for this moment. No matter how much she wanted to hate him, she loved this man. She was too weak to fight him, her senses muddled by his presence so that she couldn't think rationally. He had taught her all she knew about loving, and he had only to touch her to coax a fiery response. Her heartbeats matching his, Kati's hands sought the defined muscles of his back; her hips pressed forward to meet him; her lips grew warm and moist, and she found herself returning his hungry, consuming kiss with fire of her own.

Raul's full lips traced a warm path down her throat to the bodice of her dress, and before Kati knew it, he had undone the row of tiny pearl buttons and found the rigid peak of her breast. She moaned softly as his tongue tasted the dark tip, and she tried valiantly to fight the fire raging in her veins. She couldn't let Raul take her after all the months of silence between them. She no longer felt that he had the right to start such wild fires inside her. Tightly gripping his crisp black hair, she raised his head until their eyes met.

A sharp rap on the door startled Kati from her love-induced stupor. A female voice spoke in Spanish and Kati pulled out of Raul's arms and frantically tried to fit the tiny pearl buttons back into the holes.

Raul responded to the knock in Spanish, then tried to pull Kati back into his arms. "It was the maid with towels. I told her to come back later," he said in a husky voice, his dark eyes glowing.

"Don't, Raul," Kati managed to murmur, clutching her bodice together.

Raul watched her for a moment, then ran a hand through his hair. "I'll call for you at ten in the morning, Kati." Abruptly turning away from her, he left the room before she could speak.

She watched the door close before she sagged against it, her knees trembling. Raul's very nearness had been like a love drug to her needy soul. Her body was flaming where he had stroked it; his body had left a fiery imprint on hers. She couldn't see him again. She *wouldn't* see him again! She had had a narrow and fortunate escape this time. She had almost gone to bed with him, she thought incredulously. It had seemed so natural and so right to be in his arms, and she had wanted him so badly. With shaking hands, she stepped out of the voile dress and laid it across a chair. She had intended to sketch tonight, but she couldn't concentrate now. Slipping beneath the cool white sheets of the bed, she closed her eyes.

Raul was there in her mind through the long night, to torment her, to tease her, to smile at her mockingly and to hold her in his arms. And in her dreams, his lovemaking didn't stop with the torrid kiss and tantalizing caresses he had given her tonight. But in her dreams, he was still her husband . . . and he loved her.

Kati awakened early the next morning, feeling more tired than when she had gone to bed. Rising wearily, she dressed in a lightweight lavender suit with a pleated jacket. Appraising her reflection in the mirror, she was satisfied that the outfit was chic and stylish, yet showed her good figure to perfection. Having studied art and dress design, she could see that the outfit suited her well. Besides, Raul had always liked her in lavender, claiming that she looked like an exotic flower, the gentle color a pleasing backdrop for her dark hair and fair skin.

She shook the thought from her mind. She didn't care what Raul liked. She finished dressing quickly, taking only a moment to outline her lips with mauve lip color and brush her perfectly arched brows with a tiny mascara brush. She patted her cheeks to give them a hint of color, then plaited her hair into a single braid and coiled it around her head. After slipping into her favorite comfortable white strap sandals, she picked up her white purse and dashed out the door. Though it was only seven, she wanted to have breakfast and be on her way before there was any possibility of him showing up.

The dining room was busy and Kati decided to eat in the little café facing the sidewalk where she could watch the amazingly varied traffic on the busy avenue. A friendly waiter seated her and handed her a menu. This time she had more success reading it, for turning it over, she discovered that an English version was printed on the back. But this morning she didn't need the English version; requesting the continental breakfast and *café con leche,* she handed the menu back and turned her attention to the window.

There was a hint of sun this morning; it struggled valiantly to break through puffy white clouds, and Kati thought that she might need her bathing suit after all. Beneath the early morning sky, Mexico City was bustling with its busy wake-up routine: heavy traffic surged forward, stopped at the whim of a uniformed policeman, then surged forward again. Kati wondered why an officer was needed since a traffic light was clearly in evidence and in working order. She watched the long lines of vehicles, absently noticing that a large number of them were Volkswagens. Pedestrians waited for the opportunity to cross against the bustling traffic, then ran for their lives when the opportunity presented itself.

Down the way, Kati saw a news dealer selling a variety of papers and magazines; beside the newsstand was a colorful flower cart with the most gorgeous plants she had ever seen. The old woman selling the plants was doing a brisk business, and Kati wondered at the demand for flowers at such an early hour.

She smiled when the waiter served the coffee, several slices of pineapple and watermelon, and hot rolls with yellow pats of butter. She ate leisurely, enjoying her breakfast much more than she had enjoyed her emotion-filled meal with Raul. Raul! She must not dally too long over her breakfast, for she wanted to be on that bus tour far away from the hotel when he arrived for her. After all, she had never told him she would go with him; in fact, she had insisted just the opposite. He had some nerve after what he had done to appear out of the blue and think he had a claim on her time! And yet, just the sight of him had set her senses flaming.

She stood up quickly, blushing at the memory. She paid her bill with American dollars, then crossed the lobby to get some of her travelers checks converted into pesos. Placing the money in her change purse which she dropped back into her shoulder bag, she walked out onto the sidewalk of the busy street. Immediately, she was accosted by hawkers peddling their wares. One man carried a number of colorful ponchos, another rings and yet another shawls. The shawls were the item which captured her attention; embroidered with flowers in bright colors of red, gold and green against backgrounds of white, black or tan, the wraps were exquisite.

"How much? *Cuánto?*" Kati asked as the vendor eagerly thrust a delicate white shawl with dramatic black flowers into her hand.

He quoted a price that seemed quite reasonable, and Kati tried to determine how much it would be in dollars as she pretended to study the workmanship. Thinking her hesitation to be over the price, the vendor lowered it. Kati looked at him wide-eyed; she had already thought he had set a fair price, and while she paused, to her astonishment, he lowered it again.

She rummaged in her purse, hunting for her wallet, and suddenly a shadow fell across her face. Kati sensed that it was Raul before she saw him, and her pulse rate picked up dramatically. He had said he would be here at ten o'clock, and it wasn't even eight-thirty.

"You mustn't pay the first price he quotes, *querida,*" he said softly. "The Mexican street vendor loves to bargain. He doesn't expect you to pay the first quote, but, of course, if you are so foolish, he won't refuse."

She glanced at him sharply. "I didn't ask for your help," she said.

"But obviously you need it," he retorted in a quiet tone.

"I . . ." Before she could speak again, Raul began to bargain with the seller in Spanish, immediately slicing the price in half, then gradually raising the figure to much less than what Kati had been willing to pay. Before she could get out her money, Raul had paid the man and accepted the white shawl. He tried to hand it to her, but she refused it.

Not until she saw the dangerous glint in the black eyes she had come to know so well, did she take the wrap, but even then she tried to insist that Raul take her money. When she had tried twice to force him to take it, he finally let the money tumble to the ground. Kati glowered at him, but neither of them bent to retrieve it.

"Are you ready to leave?" he asked, ignoring the incident.

"I'm not going with you," she snapped, her green eyes angry and defiant. She had forgotten how stubborn and willful Raul could be when his mind was made up.

"No?" His glance raked over her attire. "You're certainly not dressed to stay in your room."

"I'm taking the bus tour at nine."

Raul crossed his arms and stood watching her speculatively. Kati squirmed uncomfortably under his deliberate scrutiny. "I know this city better than any tour guide," he said evenly. "It's in my blood. Let me show it to you."

His voice was persuasive, and Kati looked up at him apprehensively, taking in the flawless cut of his tan suit and pale beige shirt. She lowered her eyes, knowing that she really did want to go with him, and feeling herself weakening in the face of his persistence. What good could come of it? Why should she subject herself to him for two weeks, another two weeks to add to those she was already trying to forget?

"I'd rather not," she said quietly. Her eyes met his again, and she had a sinking feeling in the pit of her stomach as she saw him turn on the heel of his expensive brown shoe and stride away from her. She watched his erect figure until he was out of sight; he didn't turn back once to look at her again. A deep sense of rejection and depression settled over her, and Kati couldn't understand why it should: *she* had turned *Raul* away, but somehow it seemed like the other way around.

She looked back down at the sidewalk where the money had fallen, but both it and the street vendor were gone. Raul hadn't made such a good bargain after all, she mused with very little satisfaction.

The tour bus arrived promptly at nine, and Kati found that she didn't have time to take the shawl back to her room. She would have to cart it around all day, a mute reminder of the morning's incident. She boarded the bus along with several other hotel guests. She was both pleased and surprised to find Darren Davies among the people getting on. In a city of so many strangers, it was comforting to see a familiar face, even one that was only vaguely familiar.

"Hello," he said when he saw her. "May I join you?"

"Yes, of course. In fact, I'm grateful to see a face I know."

"Oh?" His blue eyes twinkled with interest and Kati wondered if she had been overly enthusiastic in her greeting. She wasn't attracted to him in the way he seemed to imply, but she let his look pass.

"This should be fascinating," she murmured, changing the subject as the bus pulled away from the curb. "I understand we're to see a few local sights and the University City."

"Yes. I've read a lot about the University. It really should prove interesting." His pale blue eyes swept over her appraisingly. "You look very nice today."

Kati murmured a polite thank you, then glanced out the window as the tour guide pointed out Chapultepec Park. Under graceful old cypresses and other tall trees, a number of people were taking advantage of the shade and stretches of green grass. Kati saw many *piñatas* hanging from tree branches with lots of happy, laughing children enjoying the game of trying to break the colorful donkeys, clowns, cats and ducks with a long stick. She and Darren shared the children's joy when one succeeded and a treasure chest of brightly wrapped candy spilled into waiting hands.

The park activity wasn't confined to children: vendors with handfuls of blue, pink, green, yellow and red balloons strolled around the park, selling them to beaming youngsters; young couples lounged around impressive, old monuments; older couples reclined on bright woven blankets, and there were even a few ambitious joggers so familiar in the States.

The bus moved on, forcing a place for itself in the traffic, and the tour guide pointed out a residential area of old colonial homes set on cobblestone streets decorated with quaint old-fashioned lanterns. One two-story home in particular caught Kati's attention and she peered at the red-tiled roof, the ornate arched doorways and windows covered with wrought iron. Balconies were numerous, and they too were outlined in the curving black wrought iron. Kati was surprised to see that most of the homes were hidden behind high walls and fences. She glimpsed what she could of the homes as the bus traveled along.

"That home used to permit some tours of the grounds," the guide commented, indicating the one Kati had found so lovely, "but no longer. It's a shame. It has two swimming pools and some of the most magnificent grounds in Mexico City."

Kati continued to gaze at it as the bus left the district, threading its way back into traffic. She wondered briefly what Raul's house was like, then, angry to find herself thinking of him again, she tried to push him from her mind. It was no use. She knew this was his city, and she had wanted so badly for him to show it to her. And she could not forget his stiff posture as he had walked away from her this morning. He had managed to ruin her day and not even be here. Her thoughts on him, she took very little interest in the expensive residential district known as Lava Gardens or in the world-renowned University City. She knew deep inside that she would rather be listening to Raul talk about his city than hearing the impersonal repetitions of the guide, but she also knew it was a foolish desire.

When she had planned the trip, she had had no idea

that she would encounter Raul. She hadn't intended to give him any thought. Or was she lying to herself? Had she secretly hoped that she might find something of her husband here in his city? Hadn't she come at least partly because he loved it so? She refused to explore the possibility; instead, she turned her attention to Darren's comments, but she found her concentration wavering. She heard very little of the facts on the University, and she trailed along behind the other tourists, trying to look interested; she was relieved when they all filed back on the bus and the tour guide announced that they would be returning to the hotel. Suddenly she felt very weary, and she couldn't understand her lack of vitality. When the bus finally pulled up in front of the hotel, she eagerly left it.

"See you later," she called to Darren.

"Hey, just a minute," he said, hurrying after her. Taking her hand, he pulled her aside. "How about having dinner with me tonight?"

Kati nodded, more to escape him without further delay than because she was pleased by the prospect.

"Six o'clock?" he asked.

"Fine." She gave him a brief smile as she walked into the hotel along with the others. She found a spot in the crowded elevator for the ride up to her floor, and she waited impatiently for her turn to get off. Once inside her room, she lay down on the bed fully clothed and closed her eyes on inexplicable tears. Her and Raul's brief love affair had ended seven months ago. So why did just the thought of him cause such a numb ache in her heart?

Chapter Three

When six o'clock approached, Kati was somewhat refreshed, though certainly not energized. She had slept a couple of hours, and she stretched languidly before getting up. Trailing to the large window, she pulled back the drapery and looked down on a young couple gazing lovingly into each other's eyes in the courtyard. Her gaze shifted to the window ledge across the way and she watched the pigeons billing and cooing. Even the brilliant yellow butterfly resting on the geranium in the window box had a mate. It was ironic, Kati mused, that everything in the whole world seemed to be paired just when she was feeling the loneliest. Here she was in the city of her dreams, the home of the man she loved, and all she had was an ache deep in her heart. She closed the drapery and went to the bathroom for a quick bath. Then she dressed in a simple little black dress, giving scant attention to her choice, or the fact that the valley of her breasts was tantalizingly pale against the midnight material and the slight flare of the skirt emphasized her shapely hips. Too tired to bother with her hair, she brushed it quickly and let it cascade over her shoulders in a midnight cloud. She felt a bit lightheaded, and she remembered that she had missed lunch altogether. The bus had stopped at a restaurant, but Kati hadn't felt hungry then. Slipping her feet into black high heels with a single strap across the toe, she picked up her new white shawl with its dramatic black flowers, draped it over her arm and went to the elevator.

She hoped that Darren would be content to eat in the hotel dining room, but when she saw him standing in the lobby, eagerly waiting for her by the elevator, she knew that she would be disappointed. Dressed in a pale green suit which exaggerated his thin physique, he was smiling broadly when she stepped out into the lobby. His eyes told her that he was pleased with her appearance. She glanced down at her dress as his gaze lingered on her bosom, and she flushed, wishing that she had selected a more discreet dress.

"Well," he said, "are you ready for an exciting night on the town? I've been talking to the desk clerk, and the list of possible restaurants is as long as my arm."

Kati managed a weak smile; a night on the town was the last thing she wanted, but she had agreed to dine with him, and she was unwilling to dampen his enthusiasm. At least one of them was making the most of the vacation time.

Darren began a lively recital of restaurants, and Kati held up her hand. "Please," she said quickly, "you make the choice."

Darren gave her a cocky smile: it seemed to please him unduly that she had left it up to him. Taking her arm possessively, he guided her outside to a line of waiting taxis. He summoned one with a wave, then explained to Kati that he had been warned in advance that one must set the price with the driver before the ride, or be forced to pay outrageous costs in some cases. He began to speak to the driver in halting Spanish, and Kati was impressed with how well he handled the negotiations.

Her enthusiasm heightened a bit when the taxi driver delivered them to the door of a plush restaurant set in the midst of tall trees and flowering gardens, bordering on the edge of a beautiful lake lit with subtle blue lights. They were shown to a small table out on a lantern-lighted red-brick patio. A young man with a guitar was perched on a tall stool, strumming a soft love song. Kati smiled warmly at Darren for having chosen so well.

"What do you think?" he asked with a big grin, obviously pleased with himself.

"It's lovely," she admitted. "I am glad we came. I was feeling a bit ill when I left my room, but the beauty here and this night air has revived me." She glanced at the musician. "The atmosphere is so subdued and relaxing."

Speculative blue eyes studied her face. "I'm glad you're feeling better. I don't want you to get sick. I have plans for the whole two weeks, and I hope you'll be sharing them with me."

Kati felt her mouth stiffen into a faint smile, but she didn't respond to Darren's statement. She didn't want to be pressured into seeing the town with another man while she was here in Mexico. Raul had been bad enough. The image of him striding haughtily away from her without a backward look this morning reared up in her mind, and she had to fight to keep from dwelling on it.

The waiter arrived with menus, and she turned her attention to the selection. She and Darren decided on seafood, and he suggested a before-dinner drink. When Kati agreed, he ordered piña coladas.

The delightful frothy concoction was delivered promptly, and Kati began to relax and enjoy the evening as she sipped it. Her gaze roved around the patio to the other diners; she studied a pretty floor-length dress of white satin, a ribbon of gold bordering the sleeves and hem, giving the dark beauty wearing it a majestic appearance. She made note of how the ribbon dressed the garment, and she wondered if she could incorporate such a thing into her gowns. She was reminded of the fashion show which would be held tomorrow, and for the third time, she rummaged in her purse, checking to be sure that she had the address of the fashion house. When she closed her purse, satisfied, she looked over at Darren and saw that he was concentrating on something elsewhere. She noticed that his glance wandered time and time again to a table just inside the main room of the restaurant, but she tried to ignore his obvious preoccupation with someone, or something, else. Her back was to the view he found so fascinating, and she was determined not to turn and stare though she was annoyed that he had lost interest so quickly. Men! she fumed. And women were supposed to be the fickle ones!

Darren enlightened her soon enough about the view in question. "A guy at the table right inside the door keeps watching you," he muttered in a peeved voice. "If he doesn't stop, I think I'll go inside and teach him a lesson in manners."

Kati lowered her eyes, not wanting Darren to make a scene. "I'm sure he means no harm," she murmured, not believing anyone was really purposely staring at her. How could Darren be so positive? There were plenty of other things to look at on the patio besides her. Concentrating on the music, she made up her mind to ignore the situation, but Darren continued to cast angry, glowering looks at the supposed offending party. Finally Kati's curiosity got the better of her, and she turned slightly to look, then froze, her hands clenched. Raul was seated a short distance away, close enough to have heard the conversation that passed between Darren and her. Ignoring the beautiful señorita at his side, he glared at Kati with flashing black eyes, dancing with angry glints of gold.

Kati felt a shiver race up her spine. Of all the restaurants in Mexico City, how had Darren randomly picked one frequented by Raul? She looked at Darren again, alarm rising in her as he stood up.

"See," Darren insisted. "He *is* staring at you. I think I'll go in there and knock his block off."

Kati tugged at his arm. "Darren, please," she whispered, "please sit down."

"Why should I?" he replied indignantly. "He needs to be taught how to show some respect for a lady."

"Darren," she pleaded urgently, "please!"

"Do you appreciate him looking at you like that?" he asked incredulously. "Where does he get off treating a woman so rudely? Back in Texas, we don't put up with that kind of thing."

"This isn't Texas," she practically hissed, "and that man is my husband."

Darren dropped back onto his chair as if the wind had been knocked out of him. His eyes were both amazed and puzzled, and his face blanched when he spoke. "Did you say your *husband?*"

She nodded bleakly, and suddenly feeling chilled, she wrapped her shawl around her shoulders. A pall fell over the table, undisturbed even when their meal was served. The large platter of golden shrimp and succulent snow white lobster meat was wasted on Kati and Darren. They began to eat automatically, neither of them looking back at the table where Raul sat. Somehow, his presence had destroyed all likelihood of a pleasant meal, and neither Darren nor she could think of anything to say. Once again, Raul had intruded on her life, and without even speaking, he had ruined her evening.

As soon as Kati saw that Darren had finished, she quietly asked to be taken back to the hotel. Darren stood up promptly, appearing eager to oblige. When he had paid the bill, they left the patio dining area, brushing past Raul's table quickly as though trying to avoid the devil himself. For a moment, Kati was afraid that Raul would make a scene, but although he glowered at her as she passed, he made no effort to detain her. She found to her surprise that her relief was mixed with vague and unreasonable disappointment.

She glanced back over her shoulder hurriedly. For the briefest of seconds her eye was caught by the girl's amber outfit. Kati thought her mind must be playing tricks on her for the girl seemed to be dressed in a dress very much like the one Kati had designed. Of course, the girl was sitting down and Kati couldn't see the entire outfit; besides, in her agitated state, she was susceptible to an overactive imagination. She looked back to the front again, and keeping her gaze straight ahead, she rushed from the room.

Kati didn't remember the ride back to the hotel. She didn't take a deep breath until she was safely in the elevator going up to her room. Then, unaccountably, her eyes filled with tears. Who was the pretty señorita who had been sitting by Raul's side? Did she know that she was only one of a long line of women in his life? What had happened to Brisa? Had she, like Kati, begun to bore Raul? Or was he courting both women? Kati told herself that perhaps Raul thought she should be honored that he had bothered to marry her. But then they both knew that had been the only way he could get her into his bed.

Her face flushed as she recalled the night Raul had taken her to his penthouse for dinner. He had wined and wooed her amid his lavish surroundings, and before she could clear her muddled senses, he had almost seduced her. Somehow she had held onto the shreds of decency long enough to extricate herself from his tempting arms and kisses. Ashamed of her behavior with him, she had run away. He had caught up with her out on the dark street and they had quarrelled. When she had insisted that she would not compromise her morals, she would give herself to no man without love and marriage in the package, he had told her she was silly and childish, and he had insisted that she wanted him as much as he wanted her. Although his contention that she wanted him was most certainly true, she had told him she thought it best if they didn't see each other again. But at last he coaxed her back into his arms, whispering sweet love words and vowing that he had intended from the first day he met her to make her his wife. When he told her he loved her and wouldn't press her to be his until they were married, she had believed that he truly did love her. And she had been wrong. He had only desired—not loved—her. Apparently his physical desire for her had been so strong that he had determined to claim her at all costs—even if that meant marriage—a marriage which would have no meaning to him and which he certainly wouldn't allow to hamper his life style. She had, of course, meant no more to him than the rest of his women after all. He had married her, then continued his relationships with other women as if he were still single. Tears brimmed in her eyes and spilled down her cheeks. She knew what kind of man Raul was, so why had it hurt so much to see him sitting there with that girl?

Kati was startled awake by a powerful pounding on her door. Rolling over on her side, her heart beating loudly, she snatched up her watch to examine it fuzzily. It was after ten. She had slept very late once she finally fell asleep. The pounding sounded again, and she grabbed her housecoat, pulling it on in case the impatient party had ready access to the room. She was just slipping her feet into her houseshoes when she heard the commanding voice.

"Kati!"

It was Raul, she realized with a gasp. After he had glared at her so hatefully last night, she hadn't expected to see him again. She hurried to the door, opening it just a crack; she did not really want to admit him.

To her surprise, his lips curved in a broad smile. "Good morning. May I come in?"

Her puzzled eyes searched his face, questioning the sincerity in his deceptively polite voice. "Yes, I guess so." She pulled her robe tighter around her body and stepped back. As Raul brushed past her, his eyes roamed over her figure, and she realized that the flimsy pink garment offered little in the way of concealment. The creamy swell of her breasts was quite evident and her thin gown beneath the gossamer robe molded to the curves of her hips. She could read the blatant interest in Raul's eyes, and she was glad when they came to her hair, lingering on it. She flinched when he reached out to touch the midnight strands. There was an unmistakable desire burning in his eyes as he let the strands fan through his fingers. "I love it when you wear your hair down, *querida.*"

So, she mused, it's *querida* again. Had he come here merely to torment her further? In spite of her anger, she felt a growing excitement at his touch. She flipped her hair back over her shoulder and smoothed it down. "What do you want?" she asked curtly, trying to hide the flush rising to color her skin.

A small smile played on his mouth, but Kati saw that the look in his eyes was serious. Raul Torres wasn't used to being spoken to sharply. "Today I will take you to lunch, then sightseeing."

Her refusal was quick and decisive, accompanied by a shake of her head. "You most certainly will not. I don't want to go to lunch with you, and I'm going to the fashion show this afternoon. Whatever sightseeing I want to do, I'll do on my own."

The smile evaporated, leaving Raul's lips pressed in a thin line. "Or with that stupid young American," he growled. "I came by the hotel last night. I had intended to take you to dinner myself. I had a surprise for you."

"I saw her," Kati said dryly. "And I never have liked your surprises, so spare me from now on."

"I am not in the mood to argue with you, Kati," he said coolly. "You had dinner with the American, and you will have lunch with me."

"No," she insisted obstinately. Raul hadn't changed, she told herself. She had had no idea that such a man even existed when she married him. He had honestly thought that he could snap his fingers and she would obey, and it was apparent that he still thought that.

Abruptly, Raul was through giving Kati the pretence of a choice. His hand whipped out and he dragged her toward him. "I'm afraid that I must insist," he said in a low voice that carried the faintest hint of a threat. "I have the rights of a husband."

"Rights?" she cried. "Insist? You can't make me do anything by force, Raul!" Flashing green eyes glared up into the blackness of his.

"No?" He raised his brows to punctuate the question. For a moment she feared that he actually meant to use physical strength to make her bend to his will, but his lips twisted into a taunting smile. "Then how about by persuasion?"

Before Kati could escape, his lips found hers in a lingering, sweet kiss. She wanted desperately to pull away, but Raul's mouth was too tempting, too provocative. His hand sensuously stroked her back and she felt as if she were on fire. She held herself as rigidly as possible, but she was almost to the melting point when he lifted his lips from hers, moving his head only inches from her face.

"Come with me, Kati," he coaxed softly. "You won't be disappointed."

No, she thought bitterly; she wouldn't be disappointed. Raul would be seductive and charming, and she would fall under his spell again. She would trample her pride, stifle her bitterness and heartache and pretend that their love was right; then she would give herself to him for a few hours of wild passion. When he was tired of her, or when her allotted two weeks were over, she would take her heartache home with her and begin all over again to try to forget him. She looked at his full lips, and she knew that coming here had been a dreadful error. Getting another dose of Raul certainly wouldn't help the healing process.

"Agree, Kati," he encouraged softly. "You know you want to."

"I don't want to, Raul," she lied, determined not to let him see how much his presence upset her. She couldn't allow herself the luxury of an entire day with him.

Her eyes met his and she was surprised to see that he

was really trying to get her to go with him without resorting to force or fury, both methods quite obviously in his mind. He was such a proud, haughty man, and she could see that his anger at her refusal was barely contained.

"Come on, Kati," he said. "I'll take you to the fashion show. I'll introduce you to Paco Cueto. Even with a letter of introduction, you won't get to meet him without my help. He will be surrounded by people wanting a word with him. Perhaps I can persuade him to show you the factory."

Kati hesitated. She didn't have a letter of introduction. Mr. Harris didn't know Paco that well himself. She really would like to meet the famous designer, and she would love to see the factory. But to go with Raul . . . She knew she shouldn't do it. It took all her willpower to resist him now, and if she used the fashion show as an excuse to spend the afternoon with him . . .

"Kati?"

In spite of her determination, she found herself nodding. She had weakened even while her mind continued to hammer home the reasons why she shouldn't. She drew a deep breath and let it escape in a rush. "Just for lunch and the fashion show, Raul," she said firmly. "I'll go today only if you promise to leave me alone for the rest of my time here." Her eyes met his evenly, and she saw an angry fire blazing in his. She was sure he would stalk away, and she almost hoped that he wouldn't agree to her condition.

His chin raised haughtily. "Is that what you want, Kati . . . really want?" he asked coldly.

"Yes," she murmured.

He released her abruptly. "Get dressed so we can leave."

She moved away from him quickly, this time more than willing to do his bidding before she gave in to him for more than a day. His touch set her on fire, and she didn't know how much more of it she could take without making an utter fool of herself. Only her fierce pride and the shameful memory of how he had cheated on her kept her from giving in to his every demand. Never had she imagined that he would have such a devastating effect on her after months of tears, humiliation and bitterness.

Pulling a vanilla-colored sleeveless dress from a hanger in the closet, she hurried to the bath and dressed. After brushing her teeth and washing her face, she ran a comb through her hair and gathered it into a chignon at the base of her neck. Touching her lips with a persimmon lipstick, she walked back into the bedroom and slid her feet into her white sandals. "I'm ready," she announced unnecessarily.

Raul leaned against the door watching her; his eyes raked over her, a look of displeasure in them at the sight of the chignon, but he said nothing. Kati followed when he left the room.

Raul guided her to a brown Mercedes, and Kati wasn't surprised by the luxury car. She had lived in Raul's New York penthouse: she knew his wealth put anything and everything at his disposal, including a line of women, she thought bitterly. But she was aware that he didn't have to depend on his wealth to attract the female sex: his compelling dark looks took care of that, and his arrogance only seemed to enhance the attraction some women felt for him. She tried not to think about it as he helped her into the car. Just for today, she would enjoy the time with him, regardless of the cost to her heart. She would allow herself one single day to pretend that she and Raul enjoyed each other's company with no qualifications. She looked away from him, trying not to concentrate on his handsome features, but her hand trembled as she smoothed back her severe hairdo.

"Is anything wrong?" Raul asked, watching her from the corner of his eye. Kati wondered if he could see through the facade of her indifference.

"I'm a little tired," she murmured, not willing to let him know how his appearance shook her up.

"It's the altitude," he said. "You aren't used to it. Mexico City is seven thousand feet high. It takes time for the body to adjust."

Kati glanced at him, glad for another excuse besides his disturbing nearness for feeling so faint and breathless. She looked back at the passing buildings as he began to comment on the city, and she drew a deep breath.

As Kati suspected, Raul was much more enthusiastic and knowledgeable about Mexico City than the tour guide. He told her bits and pieces about the history as they rode along the busy avenues, pointing out the contrasts in a city where everything seemed to intermingle, tall new buildings rising in old districts, red stone colonial buildings and modern designs sitting side by side, and quiet baroque-style churches in neighborhoods of noisy marketplaces.

"Mexico City has always been a cultural leader," Raul commented proudly. "The Aztecs called their city Tenochtitlan. It had a population of more than half a million when the Spaniards reached it. They were taken with the beauty of the city and the refinement. An Aztec legend which explains the founding of Tenochtitlan says a war god told a priest to settle and rule the land where they found an eagle perched on the tenochtli cactus with a snake in its mouth. The people found such a phenomenon here. The eagle, the serpent, and the cactus appear on the coat of arms of Mexico."

Kati was fascinated with Raul's knowledge of the city's history, and she wondered if all Mexicans were so well informed. She listened intently as Raul talked about architecture, pointing out palaces, monuments and churches. Her attention was attracted by the varied and brilliant vegetation, and she was amazed by the number of huge flower stalls they passed. "I've never seen so many flower stands," she told him.

"Yes, there are many of them. They're open twenty-four hours a day," he said. "We Mexicans love flowers and we have an ideal climate for them. There is year-round cultivation." He winked at her. "And, as you know, we're known for our romantic natures." He gazed at her for a moment, waiting for her response.

Kati would not meet his gaze. She *did* know, at least about Raul's romantic nature, but she didn't want to think about it.

He laughed softly and murmured, "I can see that I shall have to reacquaint you with that side of me, *querida.* And I believe I shall enjoy that."

He moved his hand to cover hers, but Kati continued to stare fixedly out the window. "I wouldn't enjoy it," she said in a tight little voice that sounded foreign to her. She snatched her hand away and locked her fingers together in her lap. This man was dangerous, she told herself, more dangerous than she had even remembered. He had already destroyed her peace of mind, but he would do no more than that. He was a bigger fool than she was if he thought he could step back into her life and have her share his bed at the snap of a finger! She wouldn't make that mistake a second time.

"Are white roses still your favorite, Kati?" he asked, putting his hand back on the wheel.

"Yes," she murmured quietly, a sudden vision of a single white rose lying on her pillow, marking the day of their marriage each month of the three they had shared together.

"Why?" he asked, his voice gently teasing. "Do you still believe in innocence and goodness?"

"No," she snapped. He had made sure of that! She wasn't that naive these days.

"Are you ready for lunch?" he asked suddenly, seeming to want to change the subject. His voice had an edge to it. "I will show you some of the most beautiful rose gardens in the country."

"Fine," she replied tersely. And despite herself, she was delighted when he pulled into the driveway of a fourteenth-century-style restaurant a few minutes later. The landscape in front consisted of neat rows of gorgeous roses, the bushes were very old and magnificent, and the flowers were saucer sized. A red roof sheltered the building, and climbing roses covered the walls. When they entered the front door, Kati was surprised to find the cool, dark structure divided into many separate rooms for dining. On each table sat a bouquet of fresh, fragrant buds. They were seated at an intimate table beneath the flames of a real torch where the dancing shadows from the flickering flame gave glimpses of an earlier elegance.

Kati and Raul dallied over fresh fruit and chicken enchiladas for nearly an hour. For some time the conversation was harmless and pleasant, centering on Mexico City's attractions. Kati mentioned the bus tour, and suddenly Raul's voice filled with scorn. "How well do you know the American you were dining with last night? He's staying in your hotel, isn't he?"

Startled by the abrupt change in manner, Kati was unable to reply for several seconds. "How well do you know that señorita you were dining with last night?" she retorted. "A darn sight better than I know the American, I can bet!"

Raul's face darkened with anger for a moment as his ebony eyes met the unwavering gaze of her green ones. The atmosphere was tense as he visibly struggled for control in the flickering light of the torch. "I hope a darn sight better," he taunted, then stood up. "Ready?"

Trembling from the suddenness of his attack, and smarting from his reply, Kati jerked her chair back and followed him from the room. She blinked uncomfortably in the brightness of the outdoors, and it was several minutes before she was able to rein her anger.

When she had calmed down a little, she smiled grimly to herself. Was Raul actually jealous of Darren? She hoped he was! It would give him an idea of how she felt. Apparently, he didn't like it when the shoe was on the other foot. Her smug feeling quickly faded. He wasn't jealous, of course. He simply couldn't imagine

Kati giving another man a look. He was sure she had spent her time pining for him. She sighed. Unfortunately, he had been right. Slowly, she drew a deep breath. What was Raul trying to prove anyway? Why was he dragging her all over the city? Did he think she would be so hungry for his caresses after all these months that she would eagerly forget his other affairs?

When they had gotten into the car, Kati looked at her watch. "The show starts at two," she said coolly. "If the place is some distance away, perhaps we should be on our way."

"Fine," he retorted, and Kati saw the way his hands gripped the wheel tightly as he drove out of the parking lot. They traveled for a while in silence, but Raul's hostility seemed to abate gradually. By the time they arrived at the fashion house, he was speaking to her civilly.

The show was held in a quaint white stucco building just off a busy street. Kati could see that the manufacturing plant was behind the stucco building, and she hoped that Raul could convince Paco to give her a tour when the show was over. She was glad she had consented to come with him when they were seated in the second row of seats. The room was packed with an odd assortment of people, including a number of photographers and members of the press; Kati was sure she would have felt shy and out of place had she come alone, no matter how much she wanted to see the show. A small, dapper man with a pencil-thin mustache, very dark coloring and black, smiling eyes walked out on the stage with a microphone in hand.

There was resounding applause, and beaming happily, he waited until the room had become quiet again before he spoke.

"Good afternoon," he said first in Spanish and then in English. "Welcome to the House of Cueto. We have some wonderful designs for you today, so look, enjoy and buy!"

The crowd clapped again and Kati glanced at Raul.

He seemed quite relaxed and interested in the proceedings, and Kati was surprised.

"For those of you who don't know me," the smiling Paco continued, "I am Paco Cueto, and this is my house. This afternoon we are going to show you some beautiful native costumes, and then we will show you what we have done to make them modern and even more beautiful. I am sure you will agree that they are the most perfect evening clothes in the country today."

When the first dark-eyed beauty sauntered out barefooted to the lively beat of a marimba band, Kati watched interestedly. Dressed in a magnificent silk dress with a scarlet bodice trimmed in black and a full skirt trimmed in scalloped scarlet with flowers and birds around the hem, the girl whirled, smiling at the onlookers.

She left the ramp and her counterpart stepped on. Kati was very impressed with the contemporary version of the native dress. It was done in the same material and same colors, but the skirt was streamlined and reached the floor, and there was a single magnificent bird on the bodice. Elegant and sophisticated and worn with scarlet heels, it was definitely evening wear.

The next dress was a floor-length white cotton, its square neck and hem trimmed in beautiful blue and red lace flowers. Kati was fascinated with the costume. The señorita with red and white ribbons streaming from her hair, a water jar in her hand, wore *huaraches* on her feet; she looked the part of a peasant. When her counterpart came on stage, however, the dress had been transformed into simple elegance. Still made of white cotton, it was gathered at the waist with a satin ribbon of red, and the hem was street-length and bordered in red satin. The model wore red heels, and her hair was in a braid interwoven with a red ribbon and coiled around her head. Kati looked carefully at the detailing and the designs. She was surprised by how much the ribbon in the girl's hair heightened the beauty of the dress. She found the outfit very appealing, but she was most delighted with the next costume.

She laughed softly when Paco told the origin of the lovely lace head covering. A French ship had sunk off the coast in colonial times and trunks full of fancy French clothes had washed ashore. The natives, not knowing anything about French fashion, had been unsure of how to wear the clothing. Creatively, they had taken the little girls' dresses of sheer lace and used them as mantillas, the neck fitting around the woman's head and buttoning under her chin, the full skirt and lacy sleeves cascading over her shoulders. It was a wonderful story and the costume was truly beautiful. The dress which followed, however, was beyond compare.

There was a low murmuring from the crowd as the model stepped forward, dressed in an ethereal wedding gown of the finest lace. It seemed to float about her body as she moved across the stage. The veil, shaped to the face, fell in a cascade of lace over the girl's shoulders. A number of flashbulbs went off as the model turned and stood before the crowd. Paco was obviously very pleased with his gown, and he knew that it was the hit of the show. "It is very beautiful, no?" he murmured.

Paco seemed to gaze right at Kati when he spoke, and she smiled. She could certainly understand his pride in the creation; it was lovely. She settled back in her chair contentedly as the bride left the stage and the show continued. She was in her element, and determinedly avoiding Raul's eyes and his intoxicating nearness, she began to wonder if she could incorporate any of the ideas into her own party dresses. How absolutely delightful if she could come up with such fascinating and innovative ideas. Southern and Mexican heritage, she mused, what a mixture. She began to imagine sketches in her mind and she had to consciously keep her attention on the fashion parade.

It wasn't difficult to concentrate when a young man dressed in a long-sleeved snow white shirt and white pants danced into the room with a beautiful señorita in native costume. Their shoes tapped loudly on the wooden floor as they whirled about, and Kati was impressed with their outfits and the modern versions which followed. Still, she and the rest of the people watching knew that the wedding gown was the apex of the show.

When the final dress had been modeled, Kati looked at Raul and found him studying her with thoughtful eyes. She looked away, suddenly realizing that she loved her husband's city and its people and history as much as she loved him. The realization was painful, for surely she would have been better off to have hated them both.

"Would you like to tour the factory, Kati?" Raul asked.

"Yes, I would," she agreed quickly.

Raul held out his hand. "Let's see if we can steal Paco away from the crowd before he becomes too involved."

Kati followed as they made their way through the people to the proud Paco. Seeing Raul, the man stepped away from the three women he was talking with. "Oh, you came!" he said happily. His smiling dark eyes turned on Kati. "Ah, this is the one. I'm so happy to meet you, señora."

So, Kati mused, Raul had already spoken to Paco, and he had intended to bring her to the show, regardless of whether she was willing or not. And Paco had been told something about her. This is the one, he said. Which one? Kati thought resentfully. She gave him a brief smile and glared at Raul.

Ignoring her look, Raul introduced her to Paco. "How did you like the wedding gown?" Paco asked, still filled with the pleasure he had felt when the crowd murmured over his fantastic creation.

"It was beautiful, simply beautiful," Kati told him

truthfully, flattered that she had been asked. She realized that Raul had been right; she would have had no chance of talking with the designer without Raul being there.

"Ah, more beautiful than yours, no?" Paco asked. "But still, you have exquisite taste."

Kati looked puzzled. More beautiful than hers? Had he seen a picture of her wedding to Raul? Her gown had been lovely, but nothing exceptional. She would have designed it herself if she had had time, but with such short planning, it had been impossible. She nodded and glanced at Raul. She was surprised to see him give Paco a warning look from beneath frowning brows. Perhaps he hadn't spoken to Paco about her after all, she reasoned. Perhaps Paco had the wrong girl. With the number of them Raul seemed to have, that certainly wouldn't be surprising.

Paco lifted his hands with a flighty, uncertain movement and raised his brows as if he didn't understand Raul's displeasure. "Well," he said quickly, "shall we see the shop?"

Dismissing the momentary confusion in her excitement at seeing the factory, Kati walked abreast of the two men and listened interestedly as Paco talked. When they had completed the brief tour, she thanked him graciously. It truly had been an inspiration to come and see his clothes, and she was filled with a sudden desire to go back to the hotel and work on her own designs. She made up her mind to do just that. Besides, it would be the only way she could possibly hope to put Raul out of her mind.

Raul drove her back without trying to talk her into seeing anything more of the city, and while Kati was surprised, she felt a surge of relief when they arrived at the hotel. She held out her hand to him, determined to stay out of his arms. "Thank you. It was kind of you to take me and introduce me to Paco."

Ignoring her hand, he opened his door. "I'll see you to your room."

"Really," she protested, "there's no need."

"I insist."

She took a deep breath. She wouldn't escape him so easily after all. There was nothing to do but let him escort her. When they were at her door, she again thanked him and told him good-bye.

"I'll call for you at ten in the morning," he told her.

Kati stared at him, her expression one of incredulity. "No! You agreed that you would leave me alone if I went with you to lunch and the fashion show today. I won't see you again."

She watched as his jaw muscle twitched ominously. "I didn't agree to that condition at all. You were eager enough to go with me when I offered you the chance to meet Paco. You had no scruples about seeing me again as long as it would benefit your career, did you? Is that the way it is? You see me as long as I can be of some help to you, then you refuse when I ask you to let me show you the city."

Kati smarted under his accusing tone. "That's not the way it was, and you know it!"

"No? Explain to me how it was then."

She blushed, and she could think of no response. She had gone with him when he offered to introduce her to Paco, and she was grateful for the opportunity to meet the famous designer, but she hadn't agreed only to further her career. She sighed heavily. There was no way to explain to him why she didn't want to spend any time with him, and he was making her feel like an opportunist for having gone with him to the fashion show. "Raul, I . . ."

"Then you will come with me tomorrow?"

She pursed her lips unhappily and clenched her hands. "Yes," she muttered against her better judgment. She didn't know how to refuse without looking as if she had used him to make a connection today, so she would spend another day with him: another day she would have to forget.

"Good." Before she could unlock her door, his lips brushed hers lightly, and he walked away.

"Oh, damn," she cursed softly as she opened the door and went inside. It was a mistake to agree. A terrible mistake, but what choice did she have? Kicking off her shoes, she picked up her sketch pad and curled up on the bed, wanting to capture the earlier enthusiasm she had experienced for the designs. But it was no use. Nothing would come to her mind except Raul's face. Breaking her pencil in half, she flung the pieces across the room. Damn Raul Torres! Why couldn't he just leave her alone?

Chapter Four

Dressed in golden slacks and a yellow and white striped blouse, Kati was ready and waiting when Raul knocked at her door Sunday morning. A small smile curved his lips when she opened the door.

"Morning," he drawled. "Are you ready, or would you like some breakfast?"

"No, thank you. I've already eaten."

"Good. We'll be on our way then."

Raul led her to the car, and an awkward silence settled in. Neither of them had much to say until they reached their destination. "Xochimilco," Raul said, carefully enunciating the impossible-sounding word. "The floating gardens."

Kati felt a thrill of excitement race through her as they got out of the car and walked past a huge marketplace filled with shoppers, goods and vendors. Looking over her shoulder longingly, she decided she would much rather shop than see the floating gardens, but when she saw a canal full of flower-decked gondola-type boats, she changed her mind.

"The boats are called *trajineras,*" Raul said, taking her hand to help her aboard a gently rocking vessel. He handed a bill to the boy who stood at the front of the boat holding a long pole. Kati was sure he had paid to ensure their privacy, for there were a number of seats, and she was secretly grateful that they would be alone.

The sun was behind the clouds and she settled down in the long narrow boat for the ride down the peaceful, poplar-shaded canals. She soon saw that business was carried on even in the dark waters: an old lady paddled a canoe filled with fresh cut flowers; in another boat, a boy and a woman were cooking ears of fresh yellow corn; in yet another boat, a man was holding up serapes, but Kati's eyes strayed to a boat filled with mariachis. They looked quite impressive in their black costumes and big black sombreros. Raul handed one of the band players some money, and they floated alongside Kati and Raul's boat, serenading them with a soft Mexican love song.

"What is the song about?" Kati asked. She lowered her eyes when Raul began to repeat the words to her in English, his voice deep and very seductive. She blushed with the memory of the times Raul had whispered love words to her in that husky voice, and she quickly turned her attention to the band. One man smiled knowingly at her as he played his guitar, and Kati was sure he saw her and Raul as lovers. A bitterness rose in her heart because it wasn't true, and she looked at the peddlers, not wanting to hear any more of Raul's words or see the band's smiling faces. Still, she was disappointed when they finally paddled away to serenade other boaters.

Kati's eyes met his and she found that he was watching her intently. "The flowers are beautiful," she mused, looking back at the islands.

"Yes," Raul agreed. "The Indians raise them to sell in the city. The islands originally were rafts made of twigs and covered with a layer of earth. Flowers were planted there and usually a small hut was constructed. Eventually the flowers took root and now these seem to be natural islands."

"They're fascinating," Kati said. "I've never heard of them."

"I have much to teach you, Kati," he murmured low, his dark eyes searching hers. "You shouldn't have run away."

Kati was glad for a distraction when the boy maneuvered the boat down another long canal. They passed another woman selling fresh cut flowers, and Raul called out to her. She skillfully guided her boat alongside theirs, and Raul selected a single snow white carnation. When he had paid the woman and the boats had parted, he slid dangerously near to Kati, turned her head toward him and slipped the white carnation behind her ear. She reached up to touch the flower and when she did, Raul dropped a brief, sweet, tantalizing kiss on her parted lips.

"Don't," she murmured, turning away and trying desperately not to fall under the magic of his spell. She sharply reminded herself that she wasn't the first girl he had wooed in this romantic setting, and she surely wouldn't be the last, but her silly heart refused to listen. It was beating wildly at his nearness. Kati breathed a sigh of relief when the boy turned the boat around and headed back to the dock. She felt only a twinge of regret when the ride came to an end; it had been quite beautiful and exciting, and Raul had been at his most suave and charming. But therein had lain the danger; Kati needed to be a safe distance from him to remember how she despised him and to remember that she was only one of the women he gave this special treatment to.

"Do you want to shop?" He indicated the marketplace as they stepped off the boat, his hand holding her arm protectively.

"Could we?" she asked, moving away from him. His nearness was much too provocative.

"Of course, *querida.* Your wish is my desire."

Kati looked at him coldly and nearly gave in to her impulse to argue that particular point, but she had agreed to this outing and she didn't want to spend the day exchanging unpleasantries with him. She smiled and let him lead her to the rows of open-air stalls. Her breath caught in her throat as she approached: everything imaginable was available. Her eyes skimmed along the lines strung between trees where lovely hand-embroidered dresses and colorful fancy blouses danced gently in the slight breeze. Under the clotheslines were tables laden with treasures: ornate and simple jewelry of gold and silver, gleaming copper pots, lamps of every shape, brightly painted plates and pottery, paper flowers so real in appearance that they seemed to have a fragrance, and pretty paintings of every description. Kati was almost overwhelmed by her desire to have one of everything. She gazed admiringly at the attractive native dresses, all in a tempting row. An amber one caught her eye, and she was suddenly reminded of the beautiful señorita who had dined with Raul when she had dined with Darren.

"What shall we shop for?" Raul asked.

Kati brought her attention back to the matter at hand. "All of it!" she said. "Oh, this does a woman's heart good."

Raul smiled at her as he guided her to some colorful paintings. "This would be lovely framed," he said, picking up one of a beautiful bird in scarlet and gold. "It is done on fig leaf paper. Feel it."

Taking the thin sheet in hand, Kati found that it was very much like the one her uncle had given her, which she had treasured. She was delighted with both the painting and the texture of the paper. "I want to buy some," she said.

"Good. May I help select them?"

She looked up at him quickly, experiencing a silly weakness when she saw that he was gazing down into her eyes. She really didn't want his help. She would have enough things to forget without looking at her paintings and being reminded of him. She knew just the spot in the living room where she wanted to hang them, and she didn't want to think of Raul each and every time she entered the apartment, but she was unwilling to spoil the light mood by refusing. "Yes, if you show good taste," she teased gently.

He winked at her. "I've always shown good taste, Kati . . . especially in my women."

"Which ones?" she asked tartly.

Raul looked at her with dark, brooding eyes. "I beg your pardon?"

"Which ones do you like?" she asked, softening her tone as she gazed at the many paintings, but they both knew she hadn't meant her question to refer to the paintings.

Raul picked up several and studied them while the vendor looked on eagerly, offering comments and urging Kati to consider several others. Raul selected three from the ones in his hand and gave them to her. She had to agree that his taste was flawless as she examined the detailed red and white flowers, the bird she had admired and an assortment of brilliant feathers.

"They're beautiful," she murmured. "I'll take them."

He laughed lightly. "I'm glad you approve." He reached for his wallet, but Kati handed the vendor a bill before Raul could pay him. The man took the money quickly, averting a dispute, and gave Kati change. She pretended not to notice the scowl on Raul's handsome face.

They had just walked to the next shop when he looked up at the sky and asked, "Do you have your bathing suit with you?"

Puzzled, Kati glanced at him, then followed the direction of his gaze. The first big warning drops of rain had begun to fall. She gasped as dark clouds suddenly opened up to pour rain down on them. The dark summer sky lit up as a brilliant flash of lightning zigzagged across it.

"Run!" Raul urged, tugging at her hand, but it was no use. They were some distance from the car, and they were thoroughly drenched by the time they reached it and climbed inside.

"Oh no!" Kati cried unhappily, looking down at the wet paintings. "Raul, they're ruined."

"It doesn't matter," he said consolingly. "We'll buy some more."

"But we chose them so carefully."

"Yes, we did," he agreed, "but we may find others we like even better. One never knows until one explores all the choices."

"No, one doesn't, does one?" Kati asked mockingly. She was referring to Raul's inability to be satisfied with one woman, but if he recognized the goading beneath the statement, he refused to respond.

"Do you remember the last time we were caught in the rain, Kati?" he asked.

"No!" she replied curtly. She didn't want to remember, but of course she did. A bittersweet scene of that day played in the shadows of her mind. They had been in Central Park in New York and a rain storm had sprung up suddenly, soaking them to the skin. Kati had been miserable, but Raul had saved the day by taking her in his arms to warm her. Shaking her head slightly, Kati forced herself to suppress the memory. She peered out of the rain-drenched car window and realized that she had no idea where they were. When Raul left the busy streets, she was surprised to see that they were in the exclusive old colonial district the bus had toured Friday. She remembered the homes, and she gazed at them intently, looking for the one she had found so appealing. As suddenly as the rains had begun, they stopped. When the sun peeked through the clouds and the rain disappeared from the windows, Kati was able to see quite clearly. For the first time, she noticed the tall shards of colored glass projecting from the high walls and thick fences.

"Why is the glass on the walls, Raul?" she asked curiously and softly, wanting to take away the sting of her last reply.

"To keep out burglars," he explained.

"Indeed," Kati murmured quietly, but she found the idea appalling. She had no doubt, however, that it would discourage prowlers.

They approached the old colonial house she had taken such an interest in yesterday, and she turned to Raul. "Do you know who lives here? The house is lovely. The tour guide said there are two swimming pools and that in the past tourists were allowed inside the gates to see the magnificent grounds."

An odd smile curved Raul's lips. He touched an electronic gadget on the dash and the wrought iron gates swung open. "I do. I live here, along with my father," he said, guiding the car through the narrow entrance.

"I see," Kati barely managed to whisper. She was sorry she had asked, but she had had no way of knowing that this was the Torres home. Raul had mentioned it numerous times, but she had never seen a picture of it. It still took a minute for his response to sink in. "Then why are we here?" she asked at last.

Raul's tone was biting when he replied. "Why, Kati? Do you object to seeing my home?"

She swallowed hard. She didn't want to see this house, his most prized possession, the symbol of his heritage. "I see no need," she replied evenly. "Please take me back to my hotel."

"No need?"

Kati nodded.

Raul's eyes raked over her wet clothing and damp hair. "If I'm not mistaken, you're wet from head to toe. We can change here."

"Into what?" Kati rasped, a panicky sensation rising at the prospect of actually going inside.

"Into dry clothing, of course."

"I have nothing to change into," she insisted. "Please take me to my hotel."

Ignoring her request, Raul got out and walked around to her side of the car. "Stop being silly, Kati. You can slip into anything until your things dry. It won't be the first time you've worn a robe of mine. Besides, it's time you met Father."

Kati looked up when José Adriano, the man who had met her at the airport, appeared from nowhere. "Shall I put the car away?" he asked.

Kati felt a blush of color rise to her cheeks as she gripped the ruined paintings. She had little choice but to follow Raul in, but she would rather have done almost anything else. She wasn't in the mood or condition to meet his father, and she saw no need to. Reluctantly, she walked up the steps to the house.

Even though she had expected grandeur, she wasn't prepared for the beauty of his home. Original Rivera paintings hung on the walls, Moorish-design area rugs covered natural stone floors, and everywhere Kati looked were pieces of antique Spanish furniture and exquisite Mexican artwork, all carefully blending to create an elegant but warm and inviting atmosphere.

"It's lovely," she murmured simply, walking beside Raul as he left the living room. Kati barely closed her lips on a gasp as she looked beyond a ceiling-high archway to wrought iron bannisters bordering marble steps that separated at a landing to curve off in different directions. A thin, smiling woman appeared before they could walk up the steps.

"Señor Torres!" she cried. "You're soaked! Can I get anything for you?"

"No, thank you, Guadalupe," Raul replied. "Kati," he said, turning to her, "this is my housekeeper, Guadalupe. Guadalupe, my wife, Kati."

Kati felt her cheeks turn scarlet. He didn't have to introduce her as his wife. She tried to smile as the woman's eyes met hers. He turned back to the stairs, and Kati followed him up to a beautiful room at the top of the stairway. The walls were a cool, buttercup yellow, as was the bedspread on the ornate brass bed. Velvet draperies hung at the windows. Large, magnificent oak furniture filled the room: a bureau, an antique desk with glass windows and a vanity with a marble top.

A rust rug lay at her feet. Her eyes roamed around the room, trying to absorb the sight of so much elegance. Suddenly her gaze rested on something very familiar; she stepped closer to inspect it. Beside the door of a walk-in closet stood her blue suitcase, and it was empty.

"What is my suitcase doing here?" she demanded hotly, whirling around to face Raul.

"I had José bring it from the hotel," he answered calmly.

"Why was he permitted to take it from my room?" she cried.

"I know the hotel owner, and I explained that you are my wife and that we quarrelled." She was sure that there was a smirk on his face. "Mexican men understand these things. It was no problem to get the key to your room."

"Did you explain that we quarrelled *seven months* ago?" Kati bit out.

Raul smiled smugly. "But we didn't."

"Where are my clothes?" she hissed, appalled by the way she had been treated by the hotel owner.

Raul opened the door to the closet, and Kati marched inside. Savagely pulling dresses and blouses from the hangers, she began to shove them recklessly into her suitcase, cramming in item after item haphazardly until she could barely close it. When she had managed to force it together around the untidy heap of clothing, she dragged it from the bed and started toward the door. Raul grasped her arm and pried the suitcase from her tight fingers, slamming it down on the floor.

"Where do you think you're going?" he asked coldly.

"None of your business," she snapped. "I told you before, Raul, you can't force me to do anything. I won't stay here."

"A man shouldn't have to force his wife," he said, "but if you insist, I will."

"You can't!" she cried. "You can't imprison me here!"

"Try me," he threatened. "I'm well known all over this city. You'll have difficulty getting transportation or lodging."

"I don't believe you!"

"Ah, but it's true, Kati," he taunted softly.

"Then I'll go home!" she exclaimed, unperturbed by his threat.

"This isn't the United States," he said evenly. "You'll find it difficult to get a flight out."

"I'll manage," she retorted, glaring at him with flashing green eyes.

He indicated a phone on a bedside table. "Try it."

Kati strode over to the phone and picked it up. Of course, she didn't know what or whom to dial; she cradled the phone awkwardly for a moment, then slammed it back down to rummage in her purse for the name of the airline she had arrived on, even though she knew it already. She knew it was useless without a number. She stood, unmoving, in helpless frustration for several seconds.

Raul watched her speculatively with brooding dark eyes, seeing her helplessness and her confusion. His voice was gentle when he spoke. "Kati, stop running away from me. It's foolish to flee back to North Carolina again."

She raised unhappy eyes to his, and to her shame, tears gathered in her eyes and threatened to run down her heated cheeks. Raul's features softened visibly at her vulnerability. "What do you want from me, Raul?" she asked raggedly. "Why don't you leave me alone? Why are you doing this?"

He didn't speak for a long while, and Kati stayed where she was, waiting for his answer. Finally he came toward her, pulling her into his arms and smoothing back her wet hair as one would soothe a hurt child. "I have my reasons, Kati."

"What reasons?" she cried.

"I had hoped, Kati," he said in a low, deep voice, "that I wouldn't have to force you to stay in my home. I had hoped that for the two weeks you would be here, you would willingly stay, but I see now that is not the case." He paused and looked into her eyes. "I have told you that my father is sick. I want you to meet him and spend some time with him."

Kati's eyes widened. "Why? What possible difference can my presence make now—after we've ended our marriage?"

"But that's just it, Kati," Raul said. "We haven't officially ended our marriage, and Father feels that you're the reason he doesn't have a grandson. He would like very much to have a grandson before he dies."

"Well, I won't have your child just to please your father!" Kati gasped.

A small smile played on Raul's lips. "Nor to please me apparently," he said, "and believe me, my father won't expect you to. But surely it isn't asking too much of you to have you stay in my home a few days and get to know your father-in-law. Besides," he added, "I can show you the city, and I find it foolish to drive to your hotel every day and have to return you there each night. Be reasonable, Kati. I'm asking a favor of you for my father's sake, and in return you will tour the city as it should be toured. Is it too much to ask that you accept my hospitality for the remaining ten days you will be here?"

Kati lowered her eyes. She dared not look into Raul's face. Yes, it is too much, she wanted to cry. Ten days! It sounded like an interminable sentence. But Raul had put her in a most awkward position, and she didn't know what to say to him. She could understand his concern for his father, and she didn't want to be unreasonable. Besides, she knew, suddenly, that she *wanted* to stay. It was hard to refuse him anything when he held her so near and spoke so sincerely and coaxingly to her. It had been hard enough to hate him at a distance. Yes, she wanted to stay, but she also knew that it would be most unwise. Very slowly, she met his gaze and stepped out of the circle of his arms.

"Say you'll stay, Kati, for an old and sick man."

She shook her head stubbornly.

The soft lines of his mouth hardened into granite. Crossing his arms, he regarded her harshly. "You will stay, Kati. One way or another. Make it easy on yourself."

She shook her head again, and she tried to turn away from him, but Raul gripped her chin with his hand, forcing her to look into his eyes. And it was too late. He saw the need for him and her desire to stay burning brightly in her eyes. His lean fingers slipped to her pale throat and stroked it sensuously before trailing down to cup her breast with a teasing caress. His lips lowered to hers, and Kati wanted to hate him, but she felt a responsive throb deep within her and her longing for him cried out to be satisfied. She trembled as his arm encircled her waist to pull her against his hard chest. The long hard length of his body molded to hers, and she felt the intoxicating magnetism of his nearness. His kiss deepened and Kati tried to fight her building passion. Finally she managed to turn her head. "No, Raul," she pleaded, her voice a quivering sigh.

"Don't fight me, Kati," he murmured. "You belong here with me in Mexico. You have the hot blood of a true Latino coursing through your veins, no matter how you wish to deny it. Only your pride makes you want to run away again."

Her skin burned where he had touched her, and she knew that he spoke the truth, but she would never admit it. "You're wrong, Raul," she managed to say.

"Kati," he said in a husky voice, "you can't lie to me. You want to stay. Agree."

Her eyes met his and she knew it was useless to deny him, but her pride was fierce. "I will stay," she finally said, "but only because your father is sick. He *is* here in the house, isn't he?" she asked, doubting his sincerity.

"Yes, of course. He's resting," Raul said. "Why don't you take off your wet clothes and soak in the tub now? I'll take you down to meet Father later. And I'll have a maid come up to hang your things." Without waiting for a reply, Raul started from the room.

Kati looked down at her clinging golden slacks and striped blouse. She hadn't even remembered that she was wet. She was actually surprised to see that her clothes hadn't dried from Raul's searing touch.

"Raul," she said. He looked back at her expectantly. "What pretext would you have used to get me into your house if it hadn't rained?"

He laughed lightly. "I would have managed somehow, Kati. I have made many promises to you about Mexico City, including one about a room where conquistadors slept. I intend to keep them all." Turning on his heel, he strode from the room.

Kati glared at the closed door, her anger rising. He was so arrogant, so sure of himself, and she had given in to his demands so easily. But she found that she really did want to meet Raul's father, and she was sorry that it would happen under such unfortunate circumstances . . . unfortunate for all of them. She would have met him at Christmas time . . . if Raul had brought her here instead of Brisa. Stripping off her damp clothes, she dropped them in a pile on the floor and walked to the bathroom. While the tub filled with warm water, she stepped in and sat down.

It was no surprise that she was trembling. Raul had done it again. He had forced her into a position which she did not desire, despite her ever-increasing fear of her own response to him. He had her where he wanted her. She despised his formidable self-assurance. She had played right into his hands. She was a fool. She was very sorry that his father was ill, and she hadn't wanted to refuse Raul's request that she get to know him, but that wasn't the primary reason she had agreed to stay.

She had agreed because she loved Raul too much to say no. Raul had persuaded her to stay in his home, but she vowed solemnly that he would not get her into the bed where conquistadors had slept. She would not be *that* much of a fool for him!

While Kati had bathed, her clothes had been hung up and the maid had vanished as quickly as she had come. Kati came out of the bathroom wrapped in a towel to find that her sketch pad and her design portfolio had been placed on the bedside table. Settling down on the bed, she picked up the pad and tried to sketch, but it was useless. Designing seemed to have temporarily lost its appeal. She closed her eyes and tried to fight the image of Raul's handsome face.

She hadn't even realized she had slept until she heard the soft tapping on her door. Opening her eyes to gaze about the room with a confused expression on her face, she raised a hand to her head and tried to recall where she was. It came to her in a sudden rush and she sat up in the bed, leaning against the brass bars of the headboard. "Yes?" she called out.

The door opened and Raul stepped inside. He sucked in his breath sharply and Kati watched him cautiously, her eyes sweeping over him. He had changed into deep blue slacks and an open-necked white shirt which emphasized his dramatic good looks. "Did you sleep well?" he asked, his eyes glowing with a strange light.

Kati nodded again, unable to trust her voice. Nervously, she ran a hand through her loose locks, brushing her breast in the process. Only then did she realize that she was naked! She had stretched out in her towel, and in her sleep, it had fallen away. The blush that raced to her cheeks came from the tips of her toes. With frantic motions, she grabbed at the bedspread, wrapping herself in it while Raul watched her with mocking eyes.

"I've seen you naked before," he reminded her softly.

Kati ignored his remark. "What is it you want now, Raul?" she asked sharply.

Her tone clearly irritated him, and he came toward her. For a frightening second, she thought he was going to rip the cover away, but then, apparently he thought better of it. "Why, Kati?" he drawled. "Are you going to give me what I want now?"

Her forehead creased in a frown, and she gripped the bedspread more tightly. Suddenly Raul laughed dangerously. "I've never had to ravish you, Kati," he taunted. His glance raked over her once more, and his eyes danced with some dark secret plan. "We'll get to that later, but for now put on some comfortable, durable slacks."

"Why?" she snapped, smarting from his retort. She had seen Raul in this mood before, and his surprises weren't always as pleasing to her as they were to him. Once, in such a mood, he had taken her to a boxing match, and she had been miserable.

"I have a special surprise for you," he admitted, a boyish grin touching his beautiful lips, revealing a youthful nature he rarely showed. "Hurry. We must not be late."

Kati wasn't eager to dampen his spirits. She realized that his good humor was fragile and might easily break . . . but neither was she willing to go with him until she had some idea what he wanted to show her. His last surprise—her clothes in his house—hadn't been exactly pleasing. "What surprise?"

"It isn't a surprise if I tell you."

"I know," she said with conviction. "But I won't go if you don't."

He frowned impatiently. "You're proving to be a stubborn, difficult guest, Kati."

"You're the one who wanted me to stay," she reminded him. "I understood that the reason was to get to know your father."

His lips tightened imperceptibly. "Father will join us for dinner tonight. Now we're going to a bullfight."

For a single moment Kati sat in the middle of the bed with her mouth gaping open as she clutched the covers to her chest. Unfortunately, this was typical of him. He really couldn't seriously expect her to go. "I will not see a bullfight," she stated emphatically.

"Haven't you enjoyed what I've shown you today?" he asked.

"Yes," she murmured hesitantly. "But . . ."

"Trust me," he said. "You will enjoy this."

"I won't!" she cried. How dare he stand there and tell her that she would enjoy seeing a helpless creature slaughtered so that a crowd of people could be entertained. "I won't go. I can't!"

"Kati," he muttered irritably, "don't be dramatic."

Her voice faltered in the face of his disdain, but she was not to be shamed into bending to his will again. "It's cruel and barbaric, and I have no intention of going no matter what you say to me. It should be outlawed."

He studied her quietly for a moment, his large dark eyes moody, the curve of his mouth sullen. When he spoke, his voice was commanding. "I want you to see a bullfight. We Mexicans love this event. Officials have tried to outlaw it in the past, but with little success. It's a national pastime. It is more humane than fishing or hunting an animal in the wild. Much more so."

"How can you stand there and say that?" Kati demanded.

"Because it's true. The bull spends three or four idyllic years on a ranch being bred for just this moment of glory. He comes from a long line of fighting animals, and he is certainly given a fighting chance against the man. The average matador gets gored twenty or more times in his career."

Kati winced at the thought. "If the matador is a fool, that's his prerogative."

Raul's mouth became set in a tight line, and Kati saw his jaw muscle work convulsively. "Don't speak stupidly about something you know nothing of. How can you judge anything if you have no exposure to it? The fight is a thing of beauty. It shows courage, spirit and skill, not only on the matador's part, but on the bull's as well. I insist that you come with me." Sitting on the edge of the bed, he leaned menacingly and dangerously close.

The tension between them fairly crackled, and Kati clung to the cover as she struggled to avoid his probing gaze. She realized that the argument over the bullfight was not really what was bothering both of them. The real issue here was their relationship; both of them fenced around the subject, neither of them wanting to expose their position. "You have no right to insist on anything," Kati muttered. "I don't know why I let you talk me into staying here. You've certainly not cared in the past whether your father met me or not." Her green eyes flashed brightly, sparkling with anger, and she turned her face away from him. She had been a fool to stay.

Raul's hands found her face to roughly force her to look at him. His dark eyes glowed with a burning fire. "You are my wife. We are joined legally. That's why you're here."

"I no longer consider myself your wife, señor," she snapped, her eyes meeting his with a new defiance as she pushed his hands away.

He inhaled deeply, and Kati watched as he struggled with his pride. His tone was curiously soft when he spoke. "But you still have not sought a divorce." Lifting her left hand, he held it up so that she had to look at her plain gold band. "You still wear my ring. You don't use my name, but it is yours nonetheless. You wouldn't be here if you didn't still care."

Kati looked away from him to stare out the window at the high wall. Her eyes skimmed along the jagged pieces of glass hidden in the beautiful scarlet bougainvillea. "I don't care, Raul," she said quietly. "I had no intention of seeing you at all. It's a big city and our paths never would have crossed if you hadn't set the meeting up."

"Jenny knew I would be in town," he retorted.

"Well, I didn't!" she cried, glaring at him. How supercilious he was! "I came to see Mexico City."

"And I'm trying to show it to you," he said, "but I am a man of limited patience, Kati, and I have almost reached the end. Don't force me into a position we both will regret the rest of our lives."

Kati felt a tightening in her stomach. There was a cruel edge to Raul's voice that she had never heard before, and his words had a frightening quality which effectively silenced any retort she might have felt inclined to make.

Raul gazed at her for a moment, then spoke more gently. "Kati, if you are unhappy with the bullfights when they begin, we will not stay, but I ask you to at least go with me and see what you think of them. You are here to see Mexico, and this *is* Mexico."

Despite her resentment at his insistence, Kati knew that her agreement at this point was vital if they were to remain civil with each other at all. She sensed the excitement which was coiled tight within Raul, and in spite of herself, she found herself giving in . . . again. "All right," she murmured at last.

Kati was sure that he smiled triumphantly when he stood up, and she was angered that he considered her surrender such a victory. "Remember that you promised that we won't stay if I'm not happy—and I won't be," she said coolly.

A half-smile remained on Raul's lips, and Kati fought down the urge to go back on her word. Still gripping the cover, she watched Raul saunter confidently from the room. Only then, when the door was safely closed, did she slide to the edge of the bed and walk quickly to the closet. Pulling a pair of dark slacks from a hanger, she found a cool, sleeveless white blouse to complement them and her favorite low-heeled white sandals. She slipped into snow white undergarments and her outfit, then deliberately coiled her hair around her head because she knew Raul hated it that way. The effect was unusually severe against her lightly sunburned skin, evidence of her morning outdoors. She shook her head in disgust at the thought of the bullfight. Raul could insist that she see it, but he couldn't insist that she stay. She was sure she would loathe it, and that would displease him. Well, she mused, it would serve him right for demanding that she go. Still brooding, Kati, determined to leave before the first bull was killed, joined Raul for the ride to the arena.

Chapter Five

José was waiting for Raul and Kati in the car. Raul opened the door for her to get into the back, then slid in beside her. It was apparent to Kati that he was trying to forget that she had taken him to the ragged limit of his patience. His smile was brief, then he began to explain the bullfights. "This is not a professional fight," he said. "The professional fight season has ended. These are amateurs, very young men, but they have had some experience in the ring. They serve an apprenticeship under skilled fighters. The best fighter will be the first to fight. He has been trained by one of the greatest bullfighters in Mexico today."

Kati nodded; she didn't want to hear about the fights. She had been coerced into this trip, and she was determined not to become interested.

"Many of the fighters have been spurned by their families, and they show extreme courage in pursuing their professions. Only the strongest of mothers can willingly let their sons go into such a career."

"Or the most uncaring," Kati retorted.

Raul glanced at her from the corner of his eye, but he didn't reply to her sharp words. "There will be four fighters and four bulls," he continued. "The fight takes place in three stages. In the final stage, the matador is given only five minutes to complete the kill."

Kati gazed at Raul, intrigued by his explanation of the ritual in spite of herself. When his eyes met hers, she peered out the window at the passing scenery.

"These bulls weigh around five or six hundred

pounds, but in the professional fights, the bull can weigh up to twelve hundred. Such a bull could easily kill a full-grown African lion. It takes sheer nerve to fight any bull."

Or stupidity, Kati wanted to add, but she found her own nerves on edge. It wasn't every man who could face so much charging fury, she was sure.

"Have you ever wanted to fight a bull?" she asked, watching Raul carefully.

"Never!" he retorted quickly. "It is an art, Kati. There have been fights in Mexico since at least fifteen sixty-one. It is a skill passed from generation to generation, and it must be in one's blood. A man doesn't just decide one day that he can conquer a bull in the ring. The bullfighter is a professional like any other professional who has painstakingly learned his craft. To fight a bull, one must live a certain kind of life. Besides," he added with a slight grin, "I am a lover, not a fighter. I am too handsome to be gored and maybe killed. How would the women live without me?"

"Very well!" she snapped. Raul laughed deeply, and she despised him for it. Why was she always rising to the bait when he teased her? Staring out the window, she gave her attention to a vendor on the street. She was sure the man was selling tiny baby rabbits. As she watched him hold the furry bundles in his hands, she couldn't keep from asking, "What is he doing?"

Raul shrugged lightly. "Selling rabbits. There is no welfare in Mexico. If one is to eat, he must work. Begging is permitted, but discouraged. Anyway, only the most desperate of Mexicans would stoop to begging. We have too much pride. People must do something to earn money, so you will see many people selling all kinds of things."

Kati looked back at the man as they passed, and she felt a sudden surge of pity for him. He didn't seem to be having much luck. José made a final turn and parked the car at the edge of the arena, and Kati's thoughts returned to the coming fights. She felt a quivering in her stomach and she almost refused to get out of the car. It was too much to ask of an animal lover to view such a thing. She looked at the people hurrying toward the entrance and she glanced despairingly at Raul.

An exasperated look rode his features briefly, then he coaxed softly, "Come on, *querida*. This is the one event which starts on time in Mexico. Promptly at four." He came around to her side and opened the door. With a resigned sigh, she climbed out, and she and Raul were drawn in by the excited crowd.

Raul led her to a seat in the first row, on the shady side of the ring, and she reluctantly sat down on the cement circle. "I'll get you a pillow," he offered. She accepted, slightly amused that he wanted her to suffer in comfort. Looking all around the ring, she marveled at the layered rows of seats, packed to capacity. What did all these people find so entertaining here in this death circle? Her gaze fell on the wooden barricade inside the cement one forming the ring, and she shuddered.

When Raul returned with the pillow, Kati sat down on it, glad to have something soft between her and the cement. There was a general air of excitement in the arena, and though she pretended disinterest, she became aware of the low, tense chatter all around her. She didn't need to understand the words to hear the excitement in the voices.

Trumpets sounded the bullfight song and despite her vow to remain aloof from the proceedings, Kati gripped the edge of her seat, watching as the bullfighters entered the ring. She was entranced by the four young fighters in their resplendent suits of tights and slippers.

"It takes almost a half an hour to get into those outfits," Raul murmured low, "and the matador must be assisted. If the suit doesn't mold tightly to the body, a fold of cloth could be caught by a horn."

Kati's eyes raked over the glittering, colorful costumes, and then over the erect, boldly arrogant young matadors. They were fascinating as they took their walk across the ring; it didn't take a practiced eye to see that they were proud of their profession and confident of their skill in an ancient art. The trumpets sounded again when the fighters had completed their entrance.

Kati gasped as the gates opened for the bull to enter. As bold and proud as the matadors, the bull thundered into the ring, wearing his owner's colors, searching for his target. After the footmen called picadors had teased the bull the first of the matadors met the challenge, confronting the animal, making preliminary passes to expose the bull's strengths and weaknesses and preferred side. Kati heard nothing of Raul's low explanations: she couldn't take her eyes or her thoughts off the matador and his opponent. She listened as he called out, *"Hey, Toro! Hey, Toro!"* The crowd responded noisily. After inducing the bull to charge the cape several times, the matador boldly turned his back and walked away.

A man rode into the arena on a blindfolded, padded horse, and the bull was picked to make it lower its head. Kati winced, a surge of pity rising for the animal, yet she still watched in total absorption, not caring that Raul was looking at her with an amused expression, or that other people around her were commenting and calling out. Again the matador made several passes with his cape; the bull lowered his head and charged dangerously close to the man. Kati was unaware of the number of times she sucked in her breath at the spectacle of man and beast locked in combat. The trumpets sounded again, signaling the end of the first third of the fight, and Kati sat back, drained by the emotions she had experienced.

But the fight had only begun. The second third started with the *banderillas,* paper-decorated sticks with barbed ends. Again Kati winced as the gaily colored darts were placed in the bull's back by the *banderillero,* but she couldn't draw her eyes away from the sight. She heard Raul murmur that the *banderillas* were more for show than anything else, but Kati only glanced at him before her gaze returned to the ring where the matador was encouraging the bull to charge dangerously close. An *"Olé!"* sounded from the crowd, and Kati was astonished to see people throw scarves, hats and even a coat into the ring.

The trumpets sounded again, marking the third and final stage of the fight, the *faena.* An assistant hurried out to remove the clothing thrown into the ring. Kati leaned forward involuntarily as the bull's attention was held while the matador asked permission to make the kill. The matador then changed his big cape for a smaller one. Turning to the crowd, he dedicated the bull. Kati watched, spellbound, as his incredibly light blue eyes settled on her face; in a moment he had tossed his bullfighter's hat to her. Instinctively, she grasped it, clutching it nervously in her hands as the matador walked away. Kati was too embarrassed to turn and look at Raul, but she could feel his gaze on her. She remained rigid in her seat, the hat pressed to her stomach as she stared at the matador.

The bull was no longer charging blindly, and she was astonished by the cunning of the huge, black animal as he moved nearer and nearer to the matador, his horns lowered to seek their mark. The matador made a series of breathtaking passes with his *muleta,* each seeming to draw the bull closer yet. The skill and daring of the brave young matador brought cries and gasps from the tense crowd. Then the moment came. Kati watched, transfixed as the matador completed his most dangerous act, skillfully evading the bull's horn to strike the fatal blow.

Kati rose with the crowd, as she unheedingly shouted "Olé!" She glanced back at Raul, blushing furiously as she sat back down on her seat cushion. A fiery excitement as primitive as time ran in her blood, and she was ashamed of it. She looked away so that Raul wouldn't see her face, but she couldn't miss his gently taunting words, "*Querida,* you have become an *aficionada,* a fan. See, you must never condemn that which you are unfamiliar with."

Concentrating on the ring, Kati pretended not to hear him, and indeed, his soft voice was almost lost to her as the matador made a triumphant walk around the ring. Women threw flowers and scarves at him, and several men tossed jewelry and jackets. Kati wished fervently that she had a single rose to throw to him.

Her heart had just begun to beat at its regular pace when the next matador stepped into the ring. She was entranced again as he and then the final two matadors proved their bravery and skill against a charging, heaving mountain of animal. Kati breathed a sigh of relief when the crowd applauded the last matador who proudly completed his walk around the ring. Then the people began to filter reluctantly to the exit. Flushed and trembling from the tension and the excitement, Kati shoved the bullfighter's hat into her purse and permitted Raul to lead her to the car.

"Well?" he asked simply when they were on their way home.

Kati shrugged with what she hoped was nonchalance, unwilling to admit her enthusiasm. She had actually been appalled by her enrapture with the ritual. But Raul wasn't fooled. He laughed deeply, then turned his attention to José, who had also watched the fight.

Kati was preoccupied with her own thoughts as the two men talked. She should have been horrified by the fights—all of her instincts cried out against such a spectacle—and yet she had become one with the crowd. Against her will, she had succumbed. The danger and excitement had overcome her in the arena just as it did when Raul inflamed her senses. Like the bull, Raul, too, was dangerous and exciting; she knew she should not care for such a man, but he was in her blood. She could no more resist him than she could remain unaffected by the bullfight. Had Raul been right? Did she have the hot blood of a true Latino coursing through her veins? Did she belong here in Mexico? Did she belong with him? Was she willing to take him on his terms just to have him at all? Looking out the window, she refused to think any more about those questions. And she dared not turn them over to her heart. She had listened to her heart once before, and the pain still hadn't subsided.

Evening was beginning to slip into darkness when they reached the house. Kati glanced at Raul, seeing a hint of beard on his strong jaw as he watched José operate the automatic gate-opener. When he caught her looking at him, she averted her eyes, pretending to study the electronic gadget, but she knew by Raul's smile that he had seen her watching him. Opening her door, he held out his hand to her, but Kati avoided it as she climbed out.

She had spent too much time with Raul today: she could feel him work his spell on her as he had done when he courted her those nine whirlwind days. His presence was too overpowering, too intoxicating for a girl used to taking things slow and easy. Kati had spent her life in the South, with its patient, leisurely way of life. Raul confused her with his jet-setting, his rounds of activity, his flirting and teasing, and his free ways with the women. After the bullfights, she wanted only to sit quietly and let time slow down so that she could think rationally. She had behaved in a most unladylike fashion, and she wanted to regroup her emotions.

"The cook will have dinner ready in half an hour. Why don't you freshen up and change?" Raul asked.

He hadn't asked her if she wanted dinner; he was telling her to be ready in half an hour, but Kati didn't mind. She would relish those minutes away from him, and anyway, she was hungry. Glad for any excuse to escape him, she rushed into the cool comfort of the house and fled up to the security of her room.

She lay on the bed for fifteen minutes wondering how her vacation plans had altered so drastically. How could she spend two weeks with Raul, then go back to

North Carolina as though he were only an interesting man she had met on her holiday? How could Raul do this to her? Why hadn't he just left her to her own ends here in Mexico City? It was true he had shown her some wonderful sights which she certainly wouldn't have seen on her own or with the bus tour, but all these things would have to be forgotten. She couldn't possibly think of them without thinking of him, and her heart couldn't go through the same agony it had endured for seven months.

Rising slowly, she showered and then dressed in the simple black dress she had worn to dinner with Darren. After looking at it in the mirror, she quickly took it off. She didn't want Raul to be reminded of that evening . . . was it only last night? It seemed ages ago. And poor Darren. He had been petrified when she told him that Raul was her husband. She wondered if he had even noticed her absence from the hotel today. He had certainly seemed in a hurry to wish her good night when they returned from dinner. Kati smiled in spite of the lack of humor in her situation; Raul definitely had the power to intimidate men and woo women. It was a deadly combination.

Kati rummaged in the closet, trying to find something appropriate to wear to meet Raul's father. She was feeling unreasonably apprehensive, and she realized that she wanted desperately to make a good impression. She knew the effect the right outfit could have, enhancing both a woman's looks and her outlook about herself, and she needed all the confidence she could muster tonight. Besides, dressing for dinner would give her a chance to feel special and glamorous after her afternoon at the bullfights; only at the moment she couldn't find a dress she wanted to wear.

At last she decided on a strapless deep green velvet dress with a pleated bodice and a waltz-length flounced skirt. She had designed it herself, and the effect was very feminine and subtly provocative. After she had slipped it on, she whirled around before the mirror, feeling quite pleased with the choice. She had worn the dress once, and she had forgotten how it set off her eyes and made her pale skin look dewy soft. She smiled to herself, remembering her surprise when she had seen her dress modeled by a tall, reed-thin, angular girl. It had looked so very different on the model than it looked now as it clung to Kati's curves.

Brushing her long hair until it shone beautifully, she let it fan around her shoulders like a midnight cloud. Then she quickly gathered it and secured it with a jade clasp at the base of her neck; she didn't want Raul to think she had left it loose for him . . . even if she had wanted to. Slipping into her sandals, she walked to the door and down the hall.

For a moment, she didn't see Raul when she descended the steps and entered the elegant living room. She heard someone talking in the back of the house, and she felt the most inexplicable urge to run. Raul still hadn't accounted for his father's whereabouts, and Kati expected to meet the man face to face at any moment. She didn't know why the very thought unsettled her, but instinctively, she felt uncomfortable with the idea. She was visibly relieved when Raul came into the room with a small, very dark Mexican woman dressed in a colorful skirt and blouse, a single black braid hanging down the middle of her back.

"Ahh, good. You're down." He turned to the broadly smiling woman, and Kati thought for a second that the woman was going to step forward and embrace her. "This is my cook, Hortencia, the most wonderful cook in all Mexico, and probably the prettiest," Raul added, winking at the woman. He looked back at Kati. "And this is my wife, Kati, surely the most beautiful woman in all of the United States." His eyes were suddenly dark and solemn.

Beaming like a ray of sunshine, Hortencia took a single step forward. "How do you do?" she asked in English, the smile remaining all the while.

Kati couldn't help but smile in return, though she

was still recovering from the effects of Raul's compliment herself. He had told her she was beautiful before, but never so seriously.

"Are you ready to eat?" Hortencia asked.

Kati nodded. "Yes. I'm quite hungry. We went to a bullfight, and . . ." She stopped midsentence, appalled that she was going to babble enthusiastically about the bullfight to this woman she had never met. She raised her eyes shyly to glance at Raul, and she saw a half-smile play on his lips. She looked away quickly, stepping forward as if to follow Hortencia to the dining room.

"Good." Hortencia smiled again, then turned away. Kati didn't know if she should follow or not, and she was forced to look back at Raul. For the first time she noticed that he looked more virile and exciting than ever in a navy dinner jacket and white slacks which emphasized his lean, muscled body. He gallantly offered his arm, and Kati took it, feeling absurdly as though she were about to enter a grand ballroom. She wasn't far from wrong.

Raul hadn't shown her the house yet, and though she had seen the luxurious way he had lived in New York, she wasn't prepared for the dining room. It was most impressive: a huge, ornate table, easily capable of comfortably seating thirty, stood in the middle of the room under two lovely crystal chandeliers; all the chairs at the table were high-backed, velvet-seated and larger than usual, obviously designed so that one could linger in comfort after dinner. Two bouquets of fresh cut flowers had been placed at either end of the table. The table itself was covered by a cream lace cloth, the edges intricately embroidered in gold. The cloth fell almost to the deep brown and gold rug which covered the floor. Kati found the place settings to be exquisite. The glasses were clearly fine crystal, and the silver had been worked in fascinating native designs. The hand-painted china was obviously very old and it was delicately beautiful.

Kati had expected to find Raul's father in the dining room, but they were alone. Raul helped her into a chair at the far end of the table, and she suppressed a ridiculous urge to giggle, feeling small and silly at such a vast table. They had entertained in their home in New York, but the table had had two removable leaves; when there were no guests, it was still comfortable for only the two of them. Raul took the seat across from hers, and Kati wondered when Señor Torres would join them. She looked around the room, and she decided that she enjoyed the splendor now that she was getting used to it.

"Shall we have wine?" Raul asked, and Kati looked up.

"Wine?" he repeated.

She nodded, realizing that the atmosphere and the day had put her in a dreamy mood. The wine would enhance it, she knew, but somehow she didn't care that she was feeling very romantic. This was the way things should have been between her and Raul . . . if only he had brought her with him last Christmas instead of Brisa. Kati swept the thought from her mind before it could taint her evening. She didn't feel like remembering it just now.

She let her mind float over the day's activities, marveling that she had done so much. She had especially liked the boat ride at the floating gardens, but she had to admit that she had been enthralled with the bullfights. She felt warm at the very thought; she, who had vowed so avidly that she would find the show revolting, had become a fan as Raul had said. She jumped when Hortencia came up beside her. The cook pretended not to notice as she set down a delicious-looking seafood salad, garnished with cantaloupe wedges.

"Thank you," Kati murmured, looking up into laughing dark eyes. The woman seemed to be in a perpetual state of merriment, and Kati found it infectious. Her lips parted in a smile, and she looked across the table at Raul. She found him watching her thoughtfully, and she was reminded that his father hadn't yet shown up for dinner. Suddenly her good mood began to disintegrate. "Where is your father, Raul?" she asked suspiciously. If Raul truly had wanted her to stay in the house to meet his father, why hadn't the man put in an appearance? "You said he would be joining us for dinner."

A glint of anger burned in Raul's dark eyes. "He isn't up to having dinner with us tonight," he said coolly, and Kati was annoyed that he used that tone with her. Had he tricked her again? Was his father in the house?

"Have you lied to me again, Raul?" she demanded. "I insist upon meeting your father."

"I have never lied to you, Kati," he retorted. "I'll take you up to meet Father after dinner." He picked up his fork and began to sample his salad.

Kati stood up. "No! I'll meet him now."

Raul tossed his fork down on his plate. "He's resting now, Kati." He stood up and shoved his chair back. "But if you want to wake him, we shall certainly do it." Without waiting for her, he strode from the dining room.

Feeling less certain that Raul had tried to deceive her, Kati hung back a moment, then ran after him. If his father were in the house, the man was terribly rude for not having yet appeared if he were physically able. If he were not, then Raul was rude for not yet introducing her to him in his room. She caught up with Raul and they made their way up the stairs and down the long hall to the second room from the end. Raul tapped once, then opened the door.

Kati tugged at his hand when she saw that Raul's father was, indeed, in the room, apparently asleep on his bed. There was no mistaking the fact that the man lying there was Señor Torres for the resemblance to Raul was remarkable. "Don't wake him," Kati whispered, glancing up at Raul. She could still see the anger glowing in his eyes, and for a moment she was sure he would wake the man in spite of her plea. She watched as he pursed his lips in a gesture of annoyance, then abruptly turned on his heel, pulling her with him as he left the room. He didn't speak again as they returned to the dining room, and it was a contrite Kati who resumed dinner. She gratefully reached for her wine glass, and after she had a swallow, she almost apologized to Raul for doubting that his father was in the house. Pride kept the words in her mouth, and she was relieved when Raul began to make light conversation. She longed to ask him about his father and his illness, but some sixth sense warned her not to discuss the subject just yet. She and Raul stuck strictly to neutral conversation, and Kati found herself reminiscing over the few times they had dined alone in their own home. There always seemed to be friends, business associates, or visiting acquaintances in New York for a single day at the dinner table. Sometimes Kati could only speak with Raul alone in the privacy of their bedroom. She struck the thought from her mind as quickly as it had appeared.

Turning her attention back to the meal, she found the dessert, *dulce de papaya*—green papayas cooked to a thick, sweet paste and served with sweetened whipped cream—to be delicious, but she was much too full to eat her serving.

"Don't you like it?" Raul asked.

"Oh, yes, I do," she replied quickly, "but I've already eaten too much."

"I know just the thing for that. We'll walk in the gardens." He looked out the window at the sun; it seemed to be trapped between the clouds and the earth, and it was a warm copper color. "This is a wonderful time to sit in the cool of evening. The sun hasn't quite vanished, but the temperature is dropping." He placed his linen napkin on the table and stood up. "Ready?"

Kati wasn't ready to stroll in the garden with him; it sounded much too appealing, and Raul in any setting was too tempting for her. She wanted to excuse herself and run to the safety of her room, but she found herself laying her napkin on the table to follow him. Her heart began to beat a little faster, and there was a slight quiver in her knees when she walked. Feeling her body's treachery, she forced herself to recall the sight of the pretty señorita sitting in the restaurant beside Raul. But even with that vision, she didn't know if she could stay out of his arms. Her heart seemed all too willing to forgive the man his indiscretions.

Raul led her down a long stone corridor of many archways. When they rounded the corner, they stepped through a large archway and into the square stone patio. Kati felt her breath catch in her throat. Like the house, the courtyard was flavored with quiet splendor from colonial days long past. High stone walls surrounded it on all sides; fragrant-blossomed vines, thick and gnarled with age, almost covered the walls completely and scented the night air with a heady, sweet perfume. A solid bank of red dahlias flamed beneath one wall and filled a circle around a towering water fountain in the shape of an Aztec god. Curving stone benches, darkened with age, were near enough to the fountain to permit a gentle mist on them. Trees towered above the high walls, many of them brilliant with lavender blossoms.

"Shall we sit down, or would you rather walk for a while?" Raul asked, drawing Kati's thoughts back to the present.

"Let's sit by the fountains," she said. "It's so wonderful here . . . so peaceful. It's almost as if there were no other place in the world," she mused dreamily, walking to a stone bench, letting a light breeze lift a delicate misty spray over her.

Raul sat beside her. "I used to play here when I was a little boy. My mother loved the garden. She would have lunch served here when her American guests came."

"Is your mother alive?" Kati asked. It occurred to her that Raul had never really spoken about his mother, though he had often said that he and his father shared this home in Mexico City.

She saw the slightest change in his expression. "The last I heard of her, she was. She left here when I was twelve."

"Where did she go?" Kati asked, gazing at him intently. Why had they never discussed this subject before? How had she missed so many things about the man she had married?

Raul shrugged carelessly. "I don't know. She fell in love with one of the Americans who was visiting here. My father refused to give her a divorce or to let her take me to America. One day she was gone. I tried to trace her once, but it had been too many years."

"Oh, Raul. How awful," Kati whispered. "How awful. I didn't know. Somehow we never got around to discussing your mother."

Raul's eyes met hers levelly. "It doesn't matter. There was nothing to discuss. My mother left seventeen years ago. I wouldn't recognize her today if I passed her on the street. It seems that the Torres men tend to choose women who are very much alike."

Kati was instantly angered. Was he referring to the fact that she had left him seven months ago? "What do you mean?" she asked.

His eyes were unreadable in the semidarkness. "I think you know, Kati." Before she could respond, he grasped her shoulders and demanded, "Why *did* you run away? I want to hear the truth from your own lips!"

For a moment Kati thought she recognized genuine curiosity in his question. Was it possible that he really didn't know, or was this a cruel little game with him?

"Did you become bored with me so soon? Was your career that important to you?" His eyes were fixed on her face and she could feel the tension in his body as his fingers dug deeply into her shoulders. "Or is there another reason?"

The pain in his voice sounded real and Kati found that she was feeling guilty for having left him, just as his mother had. How ridiculous, she told herself sharply. It was *he* after all who had betrayed her. "You know why," she murmured.

"Do I?" Suddenly he released her. "If you do not wish to tell me, I will not force you to. I won't beg," he said coldly.

Kati clenched her hands together, relieved that he wasn't pressing the subject. She wouldn't lower herself to beg either, to find out why he had turned to Brisa. She didn't want to remember that he had made a fool of her, and she certainly didn't want to remind him. Dismissing the unhappy subject, she gave her attention to the garden, wanting a passive topic. "How lovely to have such a beautiful place to escape the turmoil of everyday life," she said contemplatively, though her heart was pounding.

Raul's eyes followed hers to the cool water spurting from the stone statue. He, too, seemed willing to dismiss the subject of their separation. His eyes were pensive for a moment before he spoke. "Yes, this has always been my favorite refuge from the merry-go-round of business, people and unhappiness."

Kati's eyes returned to his face, and she studied it intently. She had never thought of Raul needing a quiet place. He always seemed at his best in the whirlwind of activity that was his life. This was a side of him she hadn't seen, but she wondered reflectively how well she really knew him. Or he her, for that matter. Three months and nine days didn't qualify as a long-term relationship. She sighed. Raul hadn't given her a chance to know him, to see him here in his home, in the privacy of his garden. He hadn't wanted her here. She had come to this city on her own. He had chosen to bring Brisa with him when he came.

"What are you thinking, *querida?*" he asked quietly. His hand found hers and he lifted it to his soft, warm lips.

Kati pulled her hand away, closing it on his kiss. She shook her head, unable to reply for a moment. As silence settled all around them and darkness enveloped the garden, a variety of sounds could be heard in the vines and bushes as the night creatures made their presence known with cries and songs. A thousand thoughts tumbled in Kati's mind as she sat there so near Raul, and yet so far away. She wanted nothing more than to have him enfold her in his arms and hold her to his heart, but she knew better than to encourage him. She wouldn't be able to say no to his touch, and she couldn't stand to give herself to him under the circumstances. Oh, why had he ruined their marriage with his need to have other women? Why hadn't he taken his marriage vows seriously? His promise to cleave only unto her until death had been as empty as his words of love. And what was she doing here with him now? What did it matter that she had never met his father now that her and Raul's marriage was only a certificate hidden away in a drawer? What did Raul hope to attain with the meeting? Was his father near death? Did she perhaps present some legal or moral complication?

"What's wrong with your father?" she asked abruptly, her voice shrill in the still of the night.

Raul shrugged again, and she sensed a new tension in him. "I'm not sure. Acute depression. Disappointment. Anger. Something more. I don't know."

Kati was puzzled for a moment. "But isn't he ill?"

"Yes, he is definitely that," Raul murmured. She felt his breath on her face. "It has grown dark, Kati. We should go inside."

She swallowed hard and nodded, but she was sure he couldn't see the movement of her head in the darkness. She was ready to escape him and his provocative nearness when he murmured, "Ready for bed?"

She stood up quickly, remembering how often he had used that phrase in the three short months of their marriage. And then he hadn't been referring to sleep. She brushed the thought from her mind. Murmuring a husky, "Yes," she took one last deep breath of the fragrant night plants blooming in profusion as they spilled over the high garden walls, and she let her breath escape through her parted lips. She would have liked nothing more than to climb into bed with Raul and have him hold her to his hard body as he had done so many times in the past, but that was never to be again.

Chapter Six

In the soft light shining from the archway, Kati could barely see Raul's brief smile as he stood up. Locking her arm in his, he escorted her back to the long corridor and into the house. She sucked in her breath at his tantalizing nearness, and she forbade her heart to increase its dangerous hammering. But it was no use. She hastened her steps on the wide, curving stairs, wanting to flee from Raul as quickly as possible, but there was no way she could escape her haunting memories of the three months she had lived with him as his wife. She entered her room quickly and slid her arm from beneath his to switch on the light. She knew it would be very hard to resist him tonight and she was determined not to succumb to his charms.

Her eyes lifted hesitantly to meet his as he stood by her door, watching her with an unreadable expression. Kati wondered if he were planning to kiss her, and she wasn't surprised when he gently drew her to him. At first he only lightly touched his firm lips to her forehead, but when Kati couldn't force herself to move away, his lips trailed down to hers. One kiss, she promised herself. Only one kiss. That was all. His hands moved down her back to her hips, pulling her softly to him, pressing his warm body against hers. Just for the duration of the kiss, she let her hands find their way into his crisp black hair to fan through its thickness. It felt good to be in his arms again. It had been so long, so very long, and her body had hungered for his caresses. He had awakened a fiery craving deep inside her so many months ago, and only his touch could satisfy it. There had been no other man but him, and for Kati, there could never be anyone else.

"Kati," he whispered in a husky, passion-filled voice. "Sweet Kati."

Kati's senses tingled in response to his deep murmur. She had promised herself that she would permit him only one kiss, but her body refused to listen, unwilling to be denied his touch. She attempted to pull away, but he spoke again in that deep, hungry voice. "Kati, don't turn away from me. You belong to me. It's been too long since I've held you in my arms."

She made herself struggle, trying to be free of the steel bands that held her to his broad chest. She couldn't give herself to him. She had to be strong and resist the waves of desire surging inside her. It was true that she had belonged to him once . . . before he had wanted someone else.

"Let me go, Raul, please," she pleaded, but his moist lips moved teasingly against hers, silencing her words with the promise of more pleasure to come if only she would allow it. His tongue slipped into the warm recesses of her mouth and moved about searchingly. His hand sought the curve of her hips and wound around her back, drawing her so near that she could no longer pretend even token resistance. Her body arched against his, and she felt all desire to resist him drain out of her. She loved this man. She wanted him to make love to her. But he had made it plain that she meant no more to him than any of his other women. And once again, she reminded herself that he had married her because that was the only way he could seduce her. The wedding vows were devoid of all sincerity. Tears rose to her eyes at the thought, but Raul's seduction was stronger than her pride. Breathless, her body crying out for his love, she felt herself being drawn to the bed. Raul lowered her gently, his body following close on hers. She gave one last, soft murmur of protest, but

Raul covered her lips with his, moving against them hungrily.

Kati was gasping softly when he raised his head to gaze down into her moist green eyes with the ebony darkness of his. He seemed to be probing her very soul with his penetrating gaze. Could he see the love there for him? Did he know how his touch drove her wild? Could he feel her tremble in his arms? She turned her face from him, ashamed that she was so vulnerable with him. Had she no shame? Had she forgotten so quickly why she left him? Did she have to run away from him to keep from tumbling into his arms, indeed, into his bed?

"Don't turn away from me, *querida,*" he whispered gently, his breath warm on her face. "I know all the secret willing places of your beautiful body, and I know that you want me now. You're my wife. Let me love you."

His hands found the pale column of her throat, and caressed it gently before moving down to touch the swell of her breast. She knew she must deny him now, or she would be lost to him forever.

"No, Raul," she cried bitterly; it wasn't fair for him to use the past against her. He had violated the conditions under which she had agreed to be his wife.

"Yes, Kati," he whispered with conviction. His hand moved to the catch at the back of her dress, and she felt it slide off her shoulders. His lips found the curve of her neck, and Kati felt him ease the dress down further. His lips tasted the dark tip of her breast, and she gasped as his hand slid down the gentle curve of her stomach, creating swirls of flame in her middle. He removed the dress entirely and pulled her body against his so that Kati felt her heart pound dangerously against his chest. She moved restlessly under his long, lean fingers, wanting him and not wanting him as body and mind fought a timeless battle. His lips found hers again, claiming them in a passionate, possessive kiss. He raised his head to gaze down into her face as his hand sought the clasp holding her hair. Freeing it, he shook the masses of dark hair loose, then ran his fingers through it sensuously.

"You have the beautiful, rich hair of a Mexican, Kati," he murmured thickly, his voice husky with desire. "Even your nose is Mexican," he said, his lips playing on the slight rise of the bridge.

His words stung Kati, bringing a vision of Brisa and her dark hair sharply to mind. Was that it? Was Raul pretending that she was Brisa? Did he wish that he had a Mexican wife? Was he so proud of his race that he regretted having married her? She stiffened in his arms, wondering how she had fallen into bed with him so quickly when she had been so determined not to.

Raul, sensing her withdrawal, lowered his lips to hers again, working magic with his soft caress. Kati was sucked back into her need for him. She felt herself responding, despite the image of Brisa. She was torn between her desire for him and the knowledge that she shouldn't let him have his way with her. She wanted him desperately, but there had to be other considerations. Finally she found the strength to press her hands against his chest.

His lips trailed down her neck, taking tiny love bites along the way. Kati found her hands trapped between their bodies. "Don't fight me," he whispered near her ear. "I know that there is no other man for you, *querida.* You desire me. You know that I know it. I can give you all you need. Let me quench the fire in you now."

This time Kati was jerked back from the edge of ecstasy. How dare he imply that he was the only man who could satisfy her? How pompous and arrogant of him to think that she would be grateful for his caresses! He honestly thought she would spend the rest of her life pining away for him, unable to give herself to another man while he took a string of lovers! And she had almost given herself to him. If he hadn't made that smug statement, she wouldn't have come out of her love-filled haze until he had claimed her. She would have abandoned herself to him eagerly like all his other women, and she would have hated herself in the morning. Did he think she was so desperate for his loving that she had traveled to his city for it?

Suddenly she jerked her dress up to cover her nakedness and turned away from Raul's flaming touch. "I don't desire you!" she hissed. "I don't want you to touch me again!"

For a moment, Raul seemed unable to digest her words. His dark eyes were pained and vulnerable, and disbelieving for a brief instant. His brows merged darkly. Kati watched his moist, parted lips meet in a thin line. Then he rolled away from her and stood up, watching her for several agonizing moments. Kati's eyes raked over his disheveled appearance, taking in the open shirt which revealed a dark chest and mussed black hair. Her eyes found and held his darkening gaze. His jaw muscles twitched ominously, and for a moment Kati actually thought he might take her by force. "All right, Kati," he said in a low, growling voice. Then he turned his back on her and walked stiffly from the room.

Kati stared at the door long after Raul had shut it before she dropped back onto the bed and closed her tear-filled eyes. How had two such wonderfully planned weeks turned into this dreadful torment? Had she only been here four days? Would she really have to stay the other ten? Tomorrow she would find some way to call the airline and go home. Other passengers changed their plans and managed to leave the country. But other passengers weren't married to Raul Torres, she reminded herself bleakly. A sob rose in her throat, and she rolled over on her pillow to bury her face in its softness.

As soon as Kati awakened the next morning, she reached over and picked up the phone without even checking to see what time it was. Hoping that *0* stood for *Operator* in any language, she dialed it. At first she heard nothing but an ominous buzzing, so she pushed down on the button and dialed again. It took several seconds, but someone finally came on the line and spoke to her in Spanish. "I need someone who speaks English," she said. *"Se habla inglés?"*

"Un momento," the party murmured; then Kati heard the dial tone again. For several frantic seconds, she was sure that she had been disconnected, but finally an English-speaking operator came on the line. Kati quickly explained that it was imperative that she fly back to America and that she didn't know how to reach her airline. The girl asked the name of the airline, and to Kati's relief, connected her personally. Again Kati asked for someone who spoke English, and she was finally helped. She explained that she must fly home at once.

"I'm so sorry," the agent said. "It is the Fourth of July week, you know. We are booked solid."

"But I must go home," Kati cried.

"Just a moment," the agent replied after a pause. She put her hand over the mouthpiece, but Kati could still hear her speaking to someone nearby. When she came back on the line, she told Kati she could come down to the airport and see what could be arranged, but that she doubted that even a standby flight would be available for twenty-four hours unless it were an emergency and she could get a priority seat. Mexico City, the woman said, was the "in" tourist attraction this summer because of the reasonable prices.

Kati had a sinking feeling inside. It wasn't a real emergency. Her life wasn't in danger, only her heart. She held the phone to her ear, confused as she ran a hand through her hair in frustration. "No. No, it isn't an emergency," she mumbled. "Thank you for your time. I'll keep the reservation I have." She started to hang up, then cried, "May I confirm it now? I must leave on that plane."

Kati sensed the agent's hesitation. "It's early to

confirm, but yes, I suppose you can. What flight are you on?"

Kati sat up straighter, looking about the room for her purse. She didn't remember her flight number. "I'll confirm later," she murmured, tears rising to her eyes. "Good-bye." She slammed the phone down in its cradle and sat in the middle of the bed, nervously biting her lip. She had sounded like an utter fool when she talked to that woman. This was what Raul had reduced her to. And it seemed that she would have to go through the whole business of confirming again. She inhaled deeply. There was nothing to be done about it now. She was trapped here. She flung aside the sheet and slid to the edge of the bed. She couldn't hide in her room all day.

Walking to the closet, she scanned her clothes. There was nothing she wanted to wear, but she pulled the flowered sundress off the hanger. It had miraculously been washed and pressed. She took a quick shower, then slipped the dress over her head, smoothing it down against her shapely form. She stepped closer to the mirror to stare at her reflection: there were circles under her eyes, her pale skin was wan, her vivid green eyes had lost their brilliance. Even her rich hair had been drained of its luster. Kati despaired at the sight. This was the effect Raul had on her . . . the effect she had known he would have on her.

For seven long months she had struggled to regain the composure she had had before she fell into Raul's arms the first time and was carried away by his magnetism. It had taken the nurturing serenity of her North Carolina home to instill peace in her again . . . her familiar Southern home and her own determination to forget Raul Torres. And now just look at her: a trembling agitated mass of nerves and uncertainty. She loved Raul. She couldn't deny that. And she couldn't do anything about it, but she wouldn't be his fool again. She could never be a wife who stood silently by while her husband amused himself with a string of mistresses. She turned from the mirror in disgust. There she went again: imagining that Raul still wanted her to be his wife. He hadn't mentioned it a single time! He was probably relieved that she had found out about Brisa and run away. He had told her often what a little temptress she was; he was just trying to amuse himself while she was here. Either that or he was merely determined to make love to her in his home as he had often promised to do. She supposed it had become important to appease his ego now. She had to take herself in hand and figure out some way to stay out of his arms for the duration of the trip.

A bitter smile played on her lips. That might not be so hard after all. Raul might not pursue her so avidly now. After last night, he might take his ardor elsewhere. He had been terribly angry. As she opened the door to her room, she decided that that would be the best solution for both of them. She saw now that there was no reason to keep closing her mind to her past with Raul. She had refused to even think of him in terms of a divorce, but while she was here, she might as well face him on that matter. When she no longer bore his name, perhaps then she could finally shut him up in her mind in a spot where his presence wouldn't be so painful. He was already locked securely in her heart, but that couldn't be changed. She had no say over her heart, but she could control her mind to some extent.

When she went downstairs, she found the house empty except for the servants. She suspected that Raul's father was in his room, and she had no idea where Raul might be. Hortencia strolled out from the kitchen, beaming at her. "Good morning, señora. I trust you slept well. Do you want breakfast?"

Kati offered the cook a weak smile. "Yes. Something light, please."

Hortencia nodded brightly, then hurried off. Kati seated herself at the vast dining room table, feeling insignificant in such overpowering surroundings. She glanced at her watch. It was nine o'clock. She couldn't seem to get her body mechanisms to work. She had never been a late riser, but she still hadn't adjusted to the altitude. She wondered where Raul was, and if he had already eaten. She would like to enjoy her breakfast in peace before he confronted her. She was too weary to argue with him today, but perhaps she would feel better once she had eaten.

It was only minutes later that Hortencia bustled into the room carrying a plate of fresh fruit, toast and a steaming cup of coffee. It did look appetizing and Kati hoped that it might be just the thing to revive her spirits and soothe the irritation she felt. "Thank you, Hortencia," she murmured.

Hortencia smiled broadly, revealing two gold-capped teeth. "It is my pleasure," she replied in formal English. "I am happy to serve the master's wife . . . at last."

Kati bristled at the words. The *master's* wife, indeed! She imagined Raul loved the term. It suited him to a T. Well, his servants might regard him as master, but he certainly wasn't her master. That was part of his problem. He thought he had only to crook a finger and the whole world obeyed. Darn him! she thought bitterly. Why had she ever met him? Her life had been so simple when she had been studying dress design and dreaming her silly little dreams of fame and fortune. Maybe she had fallen for Raul so easily because her parents had just died and she had been looking for an anchor. He was an anchor all right; he had thought to drag her down where he wanted her and secure her there with no regard for her feelings. She jabbed a piece of mango and placed it in her mouth. It would do her no good to keep reviewing her mistakes.

Raul didn't appear for breakfast, and Kati began to unwind a little as she leisurely sampled the fruit and ate the toast. The hot coffee seemed to pep her up a bit, and she lingered over two cups. Hortencia was almost too eager in her desire to please and Kati finally told her she wanted nothing more.

"You call if I may serve you something else," the

woman said cheerfully, disappearing back into the kitchen.

Kati nodded, but Hortencia was already out of the room. Finishing her coffee, she rose and walked around the dining room, studying the ornate dish closets and the fine silver and china displayed there. Alongside the china cupboard was another beautiful cabinet and Kati studied the colorful earthenware pottery painted with designs and figures displayed there. Some of the pieces were shiny and black, and she gazed at them for some time, fascinated with the collection. Then she trailed out of the room, unsure of what to do with herself. She had brought her folder of original designs to Mexico thinking that she would have some time to work on them, but she didn't feel creative. It took all her energies to deal with Raul.

She hadn't expected him to leave her alone this morning. He was no doubt so angry with her that he had sought more pleasing company. Well, she didn't care. Let him. Then perhaps he would stop hounding her. She couldn't imagine why she felt a twinge of regret at the thought. She knew nothing good could come of the time she spent with Raul. And why had he asked her to stay to get to know his father? That certainly hadn't happened since the man was always absent. Kati pondered over Raul's comments about his father's illness, and then shook her head. What difference did it all make? Their marriage was over. How could it matter if she stayed two days or two weeks? Raul was determined to show her Mexico, regardless of the implications and repercussions of doing so—but why? Was it that important to him to get her in his bed once more? As determined as he seemed to do so, she was equally determined to have him show her nothing more than the city. She wouldn't be stupid enough to fall into his arms again as she had done last night. She had wanted him so terribly.

For just a short while, it was as though nothing had ever come between them. The flame of love had burned as brightly, perhaps more brightly, than ever. Love, she scoffed. For Raul there had been no love involved. He was a virile animal, giving his charms to whoever caught his fancy. And Kati had almost become one of the line of women waiting to receive them. She picked up her pace, walking faster as though she could run from the memory. She soon found herself in the old courtyard, beneath the lavender-flowered tree, the heady fragrance of newly opened blossoms all around her.

She sat down on a stone bench in the blossom-strewn old courtyard and became lost in her thoughts. She remembered Raul saying that he had come here when life was too hectic for him. The Raul who lived in this old historical house was unknown to her. She was familiar only with the part of him that was a jet-setter. She had tried valiantly to keep up with his hectic pace in New York City and thought she had succeeded rather well, but she wondered if Raul knew the secret side of her, the quiet Southern girl she really was. She had even been willing to give up her somewhat uncertain career for him until he insisted on it. Then she had felt defensive and had insisted that she be allowed to pursue it even though she had actually wanted to stay home and have his children. Kati felt that his demand that she give up her career implied that she had no talent, and even though there hadn't been a big demand for her designs, she knew that it was just a matter of attracting the right audience. Suddenly she laughed aloud at her silly thoughts. Not only did Raul not know her secret self, he didn't care about knowing. He wanted a flaming flower like the exotic Brisa to grace his Mexico City home, not an unsophisticated little Southern belle who dreamed of a more elegant time long gone.

Getting up to stroll about the grounds, she forced the unpleasant thoughts to the back of her mind. The grounds were quite vast, and Kati felt a lessening of tension as she absorbed each new and beautiful sight.

She stepped through the archway leading away from the secluded courtyard, and she found herself in the midst of more lovely gardens. The sun was finally peeking through the clouds, and Kati was pleased to come upon a large swimming pool. She decided it would be nice to take a cool swim, and she held the thought as she explored her surroundings. She had forgotten that the tour guide had mentioned two swimming pools until she entered a row of tall pine trees.

On the other side of a terraced hill was a pool larger and more lavish than the first. After seeing the second pool, Kati could no longer resist the water. Hurrying back to her room, she slipped out of her sundress, caught her hair atop her head and pulled on the scarlet pieces of her swimsuit. Jenny had given it to her for her birthday last year, and she hadn't worn it a dozen times. She checked her image, her face coloring a little at her sexy figure. She was proud of her ample curves, but she knew that an outfit need not be brief to be sexy. Often, it was the other way around, with more being more provocative than less. She had grown used to the suit because she hadn't wanted to hurt Jenny's feelings, but she would have been embarrassed to think anyone considered it in poor taste.

She smiled reminiscently. Her mother had come from a long line of Southern ladies, and excellent manners and the need for a spotless reputation had been instilled in Kati very early in life. They were a little obsolete in today's world, and Kati supposed that accounted for her old-fashioned beliefs concerning sex.

She remembered Raul's words last night. He had actually been right in a way: no other man could entice her into bed. She would share no man's bed unless she wore his wedding ring, and that was highly unlikely since she was still married to Raul. She glanced down at the plain gold band on her left hand. She had never convinced herself to take it off. Raul had put it there, and every time she had tried to remove it, she had been unable to. It was ridiculous. She turned away from her image. She wanted to splash in the cool water and forget her problems.

She ran down the stairs and out the back door. She looked back at the house as she left the patio, and she was surprised to see Raul's father sitting up on a second-floor balcony, gazing down at her. A smile faltered on her lips as she met his eyes.

"Hi," she called out a little nervously. His eyes raked over her, but he didn't respond. Feeling suddenly chilled in the warmth of the sun, Kati turned and hurried along the cobblestone pathway. Had he not heard her? Should she have pretended not to see him? After all, she didn't know the extent of his illness. Perhaps Raul was keeping something from her. She didn't know what to think, but she rushed along the path, afraid that she had imagined the second pool; she wanted to reach it before it disappeared. She wasn't disappointed when she stepped through the pine sentinels; it was there all right, cool, blue and inviting. She jumped in without testing the temperature, and it was most refreshing. As she swam vigorously, she tried to forget how uncomfortable she had felt standing there before Raul's father. It had been almost as if he were looking right through her. Determined not to dwell on it, she stroked harder.

Kati had been in the water for some time when she heard a step on the walk surrounding the pool. Raising her eyes cautiously, she shielded them with her hand. Raul was standing at the pool's edge, looking down at her, his expression guarded, his arms crossed. She braced herself for his angry reaction to last night.

"Hello, Raul."

"Kati." He nodded, his black hair glistening in the sunlight.

He didn't speak again, and an awkward and unpleasant silence settled in. Uncomfortable, Kati began to swim toward the other end of the pool. She glanced back at him when he spoke. "Running again, Kati?"

Her face turned red and she completed her lap, then

turned and swam back to where he stood. "No," she said coolly. "Should I be?"

He shrugged carelessly as if it made no difference to him. He watched her from hooded eyes for several seconds, then spoke again. "Have you been in long?" He spoke slowly and distinctly, as if he were making an effort to sound pleasant, but she could see that he was still angry.

"Probably an hour," she responded cautiously, hoping he wasn't going to say that he would join her. She swam to the side of the pool and clung to the edge.

"I didn't expect to see you here. I thought it was the children."

"Children?" she questioned, her heart unaccountably beating erratically at the single word. Whose children? she wondered frantically. Not Raul's surely, for he had said that his father felt she was the reason he didn't have a grandson.

"Yes. We have two pools, so in the past few years, we've let the servants and their children use this one. It was standing idle anyway."

Kati thought it was wonderfully kind of him to do such a thing, but she said nothing. She was still recovering from her scare. Watching Raul with cautious eyes, she waited to hear what he would say next. She knew how badly Raul wanted children, and she had been simply horrified to think he might have had them without her. She chastised herself for her thoughts—eventually he would, of course.

"Are you ready for lunch?" he asked stiffly, and Kati's eyes fixed on the unbending line of his mouth.

She nodded, knowing that she had eaten a light breakfast, and her walk and swim had worked up an appetite. Again she waited for him to speak. She knew that the two of them were treading a fine line, and they were reluctant to step over it. Instinctively, she raised her hand so that he could help her from the pool, and, as his fingers touched hers, some of the stiffness drained from his face. His hand closed around hers in a crushing grip and when she was out of the pool, he released her.

As Kati stood there before him, it dawned on her that she had nothing to cover herself with, not even a towel. She hadn't thought to bring one in her rush to get back to the pool.

Raul's eyes slid over her silently, his brow arching in approval, though he said nothing. But then he didn't have to: his eyes spoke for him, and they spoke most boldly as they lingered on her bosom, flaring hips and shapely legs. "No towel?" he asked, and Kati noticed the huskiness of his tone.

She shook her head, unable to find her voice. Something stirred in her as his eyes roved over her with open longing. Was she so enamored of Raul that a look could arouse a passionate response in her? She looked away from him, and dripping with water, she began to hurry barefoot down the walk to the house. Raul didn't match her pace, and she was sure she could feel his eyes boring into her as she rushed along. She didn't look back until she ran up the steps to her room and closed the door, then she glanced over her shoulder to be sure Raul hadn't been right behind her. She sighed with relief at finding herself alone. The room was very warm, but she was trembling like a leaf. Only then did she realize that she had run away again.

Kati stripped off the clinging, wet suit and went into the bathroom. Turning the faucets on full force, she climbed into the shower, letting the hard spray beat down on her unmercifully. If only it had the power to drive Raul's image from her mind. But with every part of her body that she soaped, she could see his face as he had looked at her with open desire in his eyes. She finished her shower and searched for a dress to wear. She decided on a demure buttercup yellow dress of eyelet lace which made her look very soft and feminine. Surely Raul's father would join them for lunch since he was obviously up and about today. Anxiety flooded through Kati briefly, and she again felt uncomfortable at the prospect. She was sure the man had seen her from the balcony, and yet he had not returned her greeting. She slipped into her dress and glanced at it briefly before she left the room. It would do no good to speculate on Raul's father.

Raul was waiting for her in the living room when she went down. To her astonishment, he had a picnic basket in hand. "Ready?" he asked. He seemed to want to let bygones be bygones, and Kati saw none of the hostility he had exhibited twenty minutes ago. She looked at her dress, then back at him. "But I thought we were going to lunch," she murmured.

"This is lunch." A semblance of a smile appeared on his face. "I thought we might have a picnic in Chapultepec Park."

"It . . . it sounds like a marvelous idea," she said halfheartedly. She didn't want to spend a romantic afternoon with him, but it was too late to refuse. And perhaps too dangerous. His anger could flare anew at any second. Her eyes met his. "Raul, I saw your father on his balcony today."

"And?" he asked coolly.

She shrugged helplessly, not wanting to tell him that she had spoken and his father hadn't. "And since he was up, I thought he would probably join us for lunch."

Raul's eyes roamed over her face for a few seconds. "No," he said at length, "but I will introduce you to him before we go."

Kati smiled faintly. "Yes, I think you should."

She followed Raul to a room downstairs where he tapped on a door before opening it. In a spacious library, Señor Torres was sitting in a big, overstuffed chair reading a book. He looked up at them over his glasses when they entered.

"Father," Raul said, "it's time you met my wife, Kati."

Kati looked at the dark man with thick black hair streaked with gray. He was much older than she had expected him to be, and he wasn't the least bit cordial.

His eyes were cold, dark and flat as they swept over her. She felt a frantic thumping of her heart and she stood very still, barely daring to breathe.

"Kati, this is my father, Javier Torres."

Señor Torres nodded curtly, and Kati murmured, "I'm happy to meet you," although in fact she wasn't so sure that was the case at all. The man didn't seem pleased with her, and Kati had to remind herself that he was sick and surely that accounted for his coolness. After all, he didn't know her well enough to dislike her, even if her and Raul's marriage had broken up.

"We're going out to lunch," Raul said. "I would like to have you join us for dinner tonight."

"I'm not feeling well," Señor Torres replied.

Kati was sure she saw annoyance in Raul's face, but his tone didn't show it. "I see. We'll talk to you later, then."

Turning abruptly, he led Kati from the room. He was curiously silent as he guided her to the car, and Kati could think of nothing to say. She felt let down after the meeting with Señor Torres, and she wondered why Raul had ever desired that she get to know the man. As they drove to the park, Kati didn't mention that she had already seen it. Raul parked the car and they began to walk along a path winding under shade trees. A man selling balloons passed them and Kati pointed to a huge yellow balloon shaped like a flower. "Look at that one!" she cried.

Raul called out to the vendor in Spanish and the man stopped while Raul caught up with him. Kati watched as he separated the yellow balloon from the rest and handed it to Raul. Raul paid for it and came back to Kati with a faint smile on his face. He tied the balloon to her wrist and she laughed softly as it bounced in the air while they searched for an area relatively free of people. It was impossible to find an absolutely secluded area. Again Kati was amazed at how popular the park was. "There are so many people," she commented.

"The park is a tradition," he said, looking at her with

serious eyes. "It's wonderful, don't you think? There are over two thousand acres with a zoo, botanical garden, playgrounds, drives, bridle path, polo games and several lakes. Anything you want in the way of recreation can be found here. Aztec kings left their statues in stone here, and if you look over there," he indicated a building behind him, "atop Grasshopper Hill, you'll see Chapultepec Castle, once the royal palace of the tragedy-ridden Emperor Maximilian and his Empress Carlotta."

Kati stared at the castle, only partially visible over the treetops. "Are there many grasshoppers?" she asked.

Raul laughed, and the sound of it had the power to break the tension that had still existed between them. She realized at once that it had been a ridiculous question to ask when faced with so much magnificence and history. She laughed with him, watching as he spread the red and blue patterned blanket on a grassy, shaded spot.

"I imagine there were many grasshoppers once, but no longer," he said, amusement twinkling in his eyes.

A smile lingered on Kati's lips as she looked up at the huge, towering tree overhead, sure that, like the castle and the monuments, it had been there for a long time.

"It's an *ahuehuete* tree," Raul said. "There are more than two hundred of them in the park. Many are centuries old, and some stand two hundred feet high."

"It's beautiful." Kati dropped down by him on the blanket and looked around her at the many people playing gaily in the park. "This really is charming, and it's so peaceful, even though everyone in the city seems to be here."

Raul laughed again. "Everyone isn't here, but most come sooner or later." Kati watched him out of the corner of her eye as he opened the picnic basket and began to remove items from it. It occurred to her that he was no longer angry with her, and she marveled at his erratic moods. Neither of them had mentioned last night, or his father's coolness toward her, and now, here in such a delightful park, those things seemed not to matter.

"Do you recall the day we picnicked in Central Park?" Raul asked, a mischievous gleam in his dark eyes.

Kati blushed. She remembered it only too well. It had been one of those disastrous times that had somehow worked out beautifully.

"Yes," she murmured, smiling shyly at him. Even though they had an excellent cook, Kati, who had never been even mediocre when it came to cooking, had insisted on preparing fried chicken for their lunch. She had been so proud of the crisp, golden Southern-fried pieces when she took them out of the basket and laid them on paper plates. They were browned to perfection, and they looked sumptuous. She and Raul had been very hungry and eagerly began to eat. To their surprise and dismay, the chicken was barely cooked and completely inedible.

New color rose to Kati's face. She had been so humiliated; she could still remember how important it had seemed as she sat there before her new husband, her first meal a disaster. She had shrugged, thinking that it wouldn't seem so awful if she made light of it. But then tears had risen to her eyes and trickled down her cheeks, and Raul had kissed them away. A rain storm had sprung up suddenly, pouring down on them as they sat there in the park, Kati's gloom hanging over them darker than the clouds. They had run to the car and had driven home from Central Park soaked to the skin.

Raul had turned the dismal afternoon into a wonderful evening by ordering two buckets of chicken from a local restaurant and finding a bottle of good white wine. They had jumped into bed in their nightclothes, hair still damp, and eaten chicken while rain pelted the window panes. Then they had made tender love long into the night.

Raul touched her hand, bringing her thoughts back

to the present. "You do remember, *querida,*" he said softly, and Kati looked down at the basket to avoid his eyes.

"I'm starving," she murmured in a small, quivering voice. "What do we have?"

Raul opened the lid of a plastic container, and Kati had to giggle when she saw the golden fried chicken. "Fried chicken in Mexico?" she asked.

"Of course," he said, laughing. "We eat chicken, too."

"But fried?" she persisted.

A smile played on his full lips as Raul opened a bottle of wine and took two glasses from the basket. Kati watched him as he poured. He handed her a glass and then locked arms with her as a wedding couple would do, holding his glass up. "To the future," he murmured, his eyes much too bright as they looked into hers.

Kati smiled, and she felt her heart beating more rapidly. Whose future? Theirs? What did Raul hope to accomplish by reliving such a sweet memory as their day in Central Park? Was he trying to court her again? Or was he just determined to sleep with her?

"Raul!"

Kati looked up abruptly, almost spilling her wine as she quickly disengaged her arm from Raul's. A heavy, smiling woman was standing near the edge of the blanket. Raul smiled warmly at her, and they exchanged a few words in Spanish. Then he turned to Kati and introduced the two of them. The woman obviously didn't speak English, and they smiled at each other and nodded. She spoke to Raul again, and Kati's glance darted to her face when she mentioned Brisa. Raul commented and then the woman nodded again and continued through the park.

"That was Brisa's childhood nurse," Raul said offhandedly.

Even though the sun was high in the sky, the afternoon began to chill for Kati. For a few minutes, she had almost forgotten about Brisa. That's how much of a fool she was for Raul. The yellow balloon bounced brightly on its string when Kati moved her arm to set down her wine glass, but the wonderful mood had evaporated. She ate her food in silence while Raul attempted light conversation.

Unlike the day in New York City, it didn't rain on their picnic in Chapultepec Park, but the day had lost its magic for both of them by the time they returned to the car. Raul had apparently picked up Kati's strained mood, and little was said as they prepared to leave less than an hour after they had arrived. It seemed that they were the only solemn visitors in the park, for laughter and gaiety continued all around them as people enjoyed the marvelous Mexican afternoon.

Raul's only gesture of dissatisfaction at the way his plans had turned out came when he opened the car trunk and slammed the picnic basket in. Looking back at the park, Kati pretended not to notice, but a feeling of guilt intruded on her thoughts. Raul had worked so hard to recreate that mood of many months ago.

Kati loosened the string of the bright balloon bouncing at her wrist. She had meant to take the balloon home with her, but it escaped from her fingers to drift off toward the azure sky. She watched it unhappily, wondering why all the beautiful things in her life seemed to vanish so quickly. Like her plans for the future with Raul, the balloon finally disappeared into thin air. Kati glanced swiftly at Raul, but if he noticed the balloon's disappearance, he didn't comment. Strangers again, they got in the car for the silent ride home.

Chapter Seven

When they returned to the house, Kati silently went back to her room. She paced the floor for several minutes, feeling childish and small for ruining Raul's afternoon. But her remorse was short-lived. Why should she care about his foolish schemes? He had ruined her life and she was sure the picnic was just more trickery on his part to get her into bed. He wasn't used to being refused, and if that woman hadn't come by . . .

She dismissed the thought. She found her design folder, kicked off her shoes and curled up on the bed. Flipping through the sketches, she found the party dress she had been working on and took it out. Pencil in hand, she began to work on the sleek lines of the middy-length dress. Suddenly she flung the pencil and sketch to the floor. Darn Raul! What was he trying to do to her? Didn't he know that he was slowly driving her crazy? She didn't want to hurt his feelings, regardless of his ulterior motives, but who would look out for her heart if she didn't?

Kati spent an hour lying on the bed, thinking about Raul and their marriage. It pained her terribly that he didn't mention reaffirming their vows . . . only that he wanted her. He also wanted Brisa, and there had obviously been others. Kati tried unsuccessfully to put the picture of the dark señorita who had been dining with Raul Friday night out of her mind. Why had he said he had a surprise for her that night? What was it? Had the girl been part of it? Or had he picked her up only after he found that Kati wasn't at the hotel? Why had Raul wanted her to meet his father? What was really wrong with the old man?

Shaking her head to clear it of the troubling questions, Kati went to her window and gazed out at the garden below. A walk would do her good, but she didn't want to chance running into Raul. She didn't know what to say to him. She didn't know why he continued to keep her as his unhappy guest when both of them were so miserable. Her vacation of a lifetime had been marred by his presence. She couldn't relax or enjoy herself under the circumstances.

Was it Raul's intent to punish her because she had dared to run away from the mockery that had been their marriage? Did his Mexican heritage lead him to believe that he had a right to as many women as he desired while she waited patiently at home with open arms? She was startled from her painful thoughts when she heard a firm tap on her door. Spinning around, she went to the door and opened it.

Raul was leaning against the frame. "What would you like to do tonight, Kati?" he asked as though the afternoon had been no disappointment at all. "We haven't even touched on the sights of Mexico City. Would you like to see the Shrine to Saint Mary of Guadalupe? A chic nightclub? The Fine Arts Palace? The Square?"

She saw a tiny gleam in his eyes, and she knew he thought to entice her with his suggestions. She shook her head. Why didn't he just give up? "I'm tired, Raul."

"Nonsense," he insisted. "You've rested all day today. You're here to see the city. You can sleep when your vacation is over. Now which do you want to do? Shall I pick for you?"

Kati felt a tightening in her stomach at his comment that she could rest when her vacation was over. Of course, she had known all along that he was only expecting her to stay the two weeks, but it reminded her all too vividly that his interest in her was only for the duration of the vacation. Her eyes trailed over his handsome features, knowing it would be agony and temptation to spend more time with him. It was ridiculous to continue to subject herself to him.

"I really want to go home now, Raul," she murmured. "Can't you arrange it?"

His eyes raked over her swiftly, a concealed emotion in their dark depths. Kati was sure he was angered by her question, but then he shrugged broad shoulders. "Even I can't do some things, Kati. To try to get you on a flight now would be like chasing the moon. You know how you Americans love the Fourth of July. It's the wrong time to hope for a flight back to the States."

Kati was acutely aware how he lumped her with all Americans, disregarding the fact that he was half American himself, and that he spent much of his time in the States. But then the Mexican in him, with its pride and arrogance, had long ago smothered the American. "But . . ."

"No objections. You're here to enjoy yourself. You have so few days. Don't you like my city?"

His city! Again that incredible arrogance. And he was determined that she enjoy it if he had to force her to. "Yes, of course . . ."

"Good. I'm pleased." His eyes met hers. "Be ready at six. We'll have a light dinner here, then we'll go to Mexico City's most famous nightclub."

Kati opened her mouth to protest, then changed her mind. She needed to have her mind occupied by something besides nagging, puzzling questions. Besides, she and Raul again seemed to have regained some measure of civility, and she didn't want to tempt fate.

When they left the house some time later, Raul drove to a tall, blue building on a busy, brightly lit avenue. Kati was surprised by the elegance of the nightclub when they went inside. The decor was a sedate but lavish blue and gray strip, including carpet, walls and chair seats. The table and chairs were quite stylishly done in dark, carved wood, and Kati felt that the club was more like a restaurant than any nightclub she had ever been in. When she and Raul were seated, she let him order a special house drink for her. It appeared to be nothing more than sweet juices and ice, but it soon had her head spinning slightly. She smiled at Raul, and there was a brilliance in her vivid green eyes.

A band came on stage minutes after Kati and Raul sat down, and the show began. She watched in awe as three muscular men painted silver from head to toe did an unusual act accompanied by exotic music. Contortionists, the men performed incredible feats that seemed physically impossible, and Kati could hardly believe her eyes as she saw them bend and twist with slow, deliberate movements. She was glad when the crowd applauded and the spectacle ended for she realized she had been barely breathing. She drew a deep breath, then took a tiny sip of her drink.

"They were amazing," she said.

"Yes," Raul agreed. "They are from here in Mexico City, but they are famous all over the world."

Kati's eyes followed Raul's when he looked back at the stage. The band started to play a sweet melody, and a small, beautiful woman with long auburn hair and gray eyes strolled onto the stage. The lights dimmed and a single bright beam focused on her. When she smiled, the crowd cheered.

"She's Carmela Castillo," Raul said, "one of Mexico's most famous singers and always a crowd pleaser."

Carmela waved a salute to her fans, and Kati's eyes swept over the diminutive beauty. Her mind seemed to be playing tricks on her: the singer was dressed in a dress incredibly like the last sketch Kati had sold. Surely she was imagining things again. She knew how much competition there was in the designing business, and it was well documented that some designers were so unscrupulous that they changed a single detail on a dress and claimed it for their own. But had they done that to her dress? Mr. Harris had said that someone very important had bought her design. She peered at the dress again, noticing the single wide strap draped low on the left shoulder, the right shoulder bare, the bodice plunging lower on the left side than the right, and the full, graceful skirt which touched the floor. It certainly looked like her design. She brushed the thought aside. She was imagining it, of course. It was absurd. It was too much of a coincidence. That couldn't be her dress, not here on this singer in Mexico City the one night Kati was in the audience. She sighed. It had been a heady thought for several minutes.

She watched as Carmela took the microphone in hand, murmuring something in Spanish in a husky voice. The crowd laughed, and Kati looked at Raul, but he didn't translate. He was much too engrossed in Carmela to bother with Kati. The singer began to sing a slow song in a husky, seductive voice which Kati found surprisingly warm and rich. It blended well with the music and though Kati didn't understand the words, she was lulled into a romantic mood by the combination.

When Carmela wandered off the stage, the light followed her as she mingled with the people at the crowded tables. Kati could see why the crowd loved her. She held hands and bestowed kisses at will, not only with the men, but with the women as well. Kati saw the sparkle heighten in Carmela's eyes when she reached their table, and she felt a twinge of jealousy when Carmela bent down to kiss Raul on the lips. It was a kiss unlike the ones bestowed on the others. Then to Kati's astonishment, she saw the singer lower the microphone while she whispered something to Raul. They were obviously sharing some intimate little secret, and Kati felt a burning resentment inside her when Carmela turned those gray eyes on her almost as if in a challenge. A smile curved the full lips.

The band played on, and Kati looked around, pretending not to see how Raul smiled at the woman, but of course the spotlight had followed Carmela to their table, and Kati looked into the bemused eyes of the adoring crowd. She wished she hadn't given in to Raul's insistence that they come. She had known their truce was fragile, but she had had no way of knowing that Raul wanted to flaunt another of his women in her face. The lights went up, and Carmela's song changed to a faster-paced one. Kati watched angrily as the singer began to saunter back to the stage. As soon as the light left their table, Kati stood up to make her way to the ladies' room. She didn't want to be in Raul's company for fear of the cruel things she would say to him. How dare he bring her here? Was it his intention to show her that she really didn't matter to him now? She fought down the tears that threatened to surface. Why did it hurt so badly? She had known for months that Raul was a womanizer and that their marriage was over.

Hurrying, Kati walked away from the table without a word to Raul. It was enough that he was attracted to other women, but it was intolerable to sit and watch him flirt with one. She wasn't surprised at her all-consuming jealousy. It was all too familiar to her. She had felt it a hundred times before and even though she was separated from Raul, she couldn't seem to stop reacting in the same old way. Pushing through the densely packed tables, she searched for the now familiar DAMAS sign, but to her dismay, she didn't see it anywhere. Suddenly she jumped when someone touched her hand.

"Can I help you find anything?" the familiar voice asked, faintly mocking.

"Darren!" Kati cried, genuinely happy to see him. "What are you doing here?"

"Oh, just taking care of business, sweetheart," he murmured with a mock Bogart twist of his lips.

Kati glanced at the attractive girl with him and smiled. "So I see."

"Kati," Darren said, "this is my friend, Peggy Carson. Peggy is staying at the Hotel Esteben. In fact, she's a fellow North Carolinian."

"How nice to meet you," Kati said, barely able to hear Darren over the noise of the band. "What part of North Carolina are you from?"

The music stopped abruptly and Kati lowered her voice instantly.

"Asheville," the girl replied.

"Won't you sit down?" Darren asked. "Or are you with . . . friends?"

Kati blushed, knowing that he was making reference to Raul. "I don't know if he's a friend, but I'm with my husband."

Darren nodded quickly. It was plain that he wanted no part of Raul, and he didn't extend the invitation to both of them.

Looking back at her table, Kati saw Raul watching her, but she made no move to acknowledge him. She gazed around the room again, trying to find the ladies' room.

"Are you lost again?" Darren asked. He turned to Peggy with a wicked smile. "I had to rescue Kati at the customs checkpoint." He looked up at her wryly. "That was before I knew she was married. I only aid señoritas in distress."

Peggy laughed.

"Actually, I'm looking for the restroom," Kati admitted shyly, laughing gently at Darren's comment. "And I am lost again."

"And I can help you again," he said cheerfully, "even if you are a señora. I have just returned from the area you seek. Yours is over there." He pointed to a far wall. "Make a left at the end of the bar."

"Thank you," Kati said. "It was nice to meet you, Peggy."

The other girl smiled, and Kati walked away.

She stayed in the restroom sitting in a plush chair in the lounge for a long time, seething with anger at Raul and at herself for caring what he did. She knew how he was. That was why she had left him. Why was she letting herself experience these destructive emotions again? What did it matter now? He wasn't hers. Apparently, he never had been.

Drawing a deep breath, she plastered a smile on her face and headed back to their table. The smile faded as quickly as it had been forced to her lips. Carmela was sitting at the table with Raul, and Kati had to suppress an urge to march out of the club into the brightly lit night. Making herself step up to the table, she glared at Raul. When his eyes met hers, his were as brilliant with fire as were hers.

Carmela rose from Kati's chair. "Hello," she said pleasantly, but she wound her braceleted arm possessively around Raul's neck, leaning down over him.

"Hello," Kati forced herself to respond through tight lips. The two women looked at each other for several seconds before Carmela deposited a wet kiss on Raul's cheek and vanished. Kati and Raul continued to glower at each other.

"Are you ready to leave?" he finally growled.

"An hour ago!" she replied.

"Not before you had the chance to speak to your American friend," he countered harshly.

"But before you had the chance to speak to your Mexican one," she replied with equal venom.

Raul stood up, his fingers biting into the soft flesh of her upper arm as he led her from the club. Neither of them spoke again as they drove back to the house.

Finally Kati could stand it no longer. "Raul, drive me back to the Hotel Esteben. I don't want to spend another night in your house."

He glanced obliquely at her as he got out of the car and walked around to her side to open the door. Stubbornly, she remained in her seat.

"Get out, Kati."

"Please, Raul," she cried. "Stop torturing me. I can't stand another hour with you! Take me back to the hotel, or drive me to the airport. I'd rather sleep in a chair until I can return home than stay with you."

His eyes ravished her face before he reached for her wrist, dragging her from the car. "Do you care so little for me, Kati?" he asked hatefully.

She smiled bitterly. If only he knew that her problem was just the opposite. She didn't hate him enough. "Yes!" she cried. "Yes! Stop tormenting me! Leave me alone!"

Suddenly he crushed her body to his, his breath warm on her face when he spoke. "I wish I could leave you alone. *Por Dios!* I would give all that I own." His lips swooped down on hers and he kissed her with a savagery she hadn't known before. Her emotions were already ragged and his passion pushed her past the limit. She felt her betraying body respond with a fire she had never experienced. Ever since she first saw him in the hotel, she had wanted nothing more than to lose herself in his love, if only for a single hour. She fought valiantly against it, but it was no use. Seeing him with the singer had only reminded her of how much she wanted him to be hers. Hating him as much as she loved him, she wrapped her arms around his muscled back and held him to her until her arms were aching.

"I hate you, Raul. I hate you," she murmured pitifully.

She heard a groan deep in his throat as he lifted her up in his arms and carried her into the house, past the startled Hortencia. Kati hid her face on his shoulder, not wanting the cook to see her in Raul's arms, but powerless to do other than as he willed. He held such a cruel attraction for her, and he had been the only man she had ever known who could drive her to thoughts of ecstasy and hatred at the same moment. Her body burned where it met the hard lines of his; she didn't make a sound as he carried her down the long corridor past her room to his.

It was hopeless to make any pretense of not wanting

what he wanted. She despised herself and him, but if any woman was going to be in his arms tonight, it was going to be her, regardless of the price to pride and heart. She wouldn't beg him to say that he loved her because she knew the words would be empty, but, dear God, she couldn't leave his arms.

He lowered her gently onto the bed, and she was flaming from his very nearness. Months of sweet, sweet dreams were going to come true for her, and she could do nothing but wait for the bittersweet ecstasy to come, an echo of the joy she had once found with him.

As Raul gathered her hungrily to him, his body pressing urgently against hers, she promised herself just this one night with him. Just this one night to touch heaven before she knew hell again in the lonely years ahead without him. Just this one night of bliss and shame. Raul didn't see the single tear slip from her misty eyes as he claimed her trembling lips, and Kati closed her eyes as she was swept along by the love for him that she could not deny.

Raul's kiss deepened into one of burning passion, and Kati found her own lips meeting the fire in his. Her arms wound around him and she pulled him possessively to her, wanting to feel the very fiber of him this one last time. Raul quickly dispensed with their clothing, and at last Kati found herself where she had wanted to be for so long, pressed against her husband's muscled body with no barriers. She forgot all about her tears and her shame as Raul led them into the sweet completeness of love. "I love you, Kati," she heard him whisper huskily as his body arched over hers. "I love you."

Kati rolled over on her side, cradling her head as she blinked at the unfamiliar surroundings. A cool breeze crept in from the window and gently played along her nude body. Grabbing the sheet in surprise, she thought about the events of last night which raced to her mind, sending color to her cheeks. She turned to face Raul, but he was gone. Slumping back against the silk pillow cover, she looked around the room.

Like the owner, it was strong and masculine, yet beautiful, with deep browns and rusts which kept the room dark and cool. Kati scooted up against the heavy wood of the headboard. Was this the bedroom the conquistadors had slept in? she wondered bitterly. And how many women had slept here with Raul? And now Kati's name was added to the list. She had done what she promised herself she wouldn't do. She had let Raul have his way as he had vowed he would.

A glint of bright color caught her eye, and for the first time she noticed the brilliant colors of the three paintings which lay beside her on the massive bed. She reached down for them, surprised that they were exact duplicates of the three paintings she and Raul had selected so carefully: the three which had been ruined in the rain. Then Kati saw it . . . a single white rose nestled in the folds of the sheet. A surge of bitter tears rushed to her eyes. She wished Raul had picked another time to give the paintings and the flower to her. They were a bittersweet payment for the sentimental night of love she had shared with him.

Leaving them on the bed, she slid to the edge, grabbed up her scattered clothes, and rushed out of the room and down the hall to her own room. Glancing at the wall clock, she saw that it was nearly eight. The bitter reality of last night's actions caused her stomach to tighten painfully. She had given herself to Raul after all. How triumphant he must be this morning. He hadn't even bothered to stay in bed with her.

He had had his way with her, and now it was business as usual for him. Spending the night with a woman was nothing new to him. That she was still his wife must have been merely incidental. Ashamed of her weakness in loving Raul at all costs, Kati trailed forlornly to the bathroom to shower.

After she had bathed, she dried on a yellow towel,

and went to her closet to pull out some clothes. She decided on a gray pair of blousy slacks, pleated at the waistband and narrow at the ankles, and a soft, clinging silver cotton blouse. When she was dressed Raul's request for her to wear her hair down sounded in her mind, but she gathered her hair tightly and pinned it in a severe matronly bun at the back of her head.

She gave herself a brief glance and was dismayed to see how lovely she looked this morning. Instead of the haggard, used way she felt, she saw a glowing, well-rested, clear-eyed young woman staring back at her, the blush of love still on her cheeks. She cursed the image that made a mockery of her troubled mind, then walked downstairs and out into the garden. She sat down on the stone bench and let the sun beat down on her face as she closed her eyes and inhaled the heady sweetness of newly opened blossoms, trying desperately to block out the pleasing sensations of Raul's caresses in the dark of his room. Why had she yielded to him in a moment of bitter jealousy and possessive love? How could she face him in the days to come? For the hundredth time, she wished she had never come here. Why had she listened to Jenny? But then she had no way of knowing that her friend was setting her up for heartache, she thought bitterly.

"*Querida,* there you are," she heard Raul call out in a low voice. She pressed her lips into a thin line and opened her eyes to stare at him, sure that he would be gloating this morning. "Hortencia said you didn't eat breakfast," he commented, coming up to stand before her.

She tried to still the beating of her heart at his nearness, and she fought down the memory of his hard body pressing so tantalizingly against hers. "No, I wasn't hungry."

His voice was light and teasing. "I was ravenous. I rose at seven and had sausages and eggs." She was sure that his eyes mocked her, yet she could hear nothing but a light, teasing playfulness in his voice. When she didn't reply, he looked at the fountain for a moment as though he were studying it. His voice was less light when he spoke again. "Are you unhappy this morning?"

Kati felt a sudden desolation as she sat there before her husband. She longed to have someone know the misery she felt and the isolation she experienced with him standing so near. It was heart-rending to love someone who didn't return that love. She felt tears beat at the backs of her eyes, and she looked up at Raul with a pleading expression. "I want to talk to Jenny this morning."

Raul's brows met in a heavy line, and Kati couldn't read the strange expression in his dark eyes. He regarded her intently for several moments, his features stern. "Won't Jenny be working?" he asked at last. "Today is Tuesday."

"She took her vacation time even though she didn't go anywhere," Kati replied in a weak, defeated voice. Jenny was the last person she should want to talk to, but Jenny was the only one who knew all about Raul, and Kati had a deep need to pour out her misery to her friend.

Raul shrugged lightly. "Come into the house. I'll place the call for you."

Kati never questioned why Raul knew the number so readily; she stood quietly by while he put the call through, and she accepted the phone when he handed it to her. To her dismay, he lingered in the room, near enough to hear what she was saying. The phone rang twice, and Jenny answered cheerfully.

"It's me," Kati said softly.

"Oh, Kati!" Jenny cried. "I've been praying that you would call. I didn't know how to reach you, and I have the most wonderful news! Don proposed! We're getting married Thursday!"

Kati was stunned by her friend's news, and it took all the energy she had to respond to her jubilation. "That's marvelous, Jenny," she replied with all the enthusiasm she could summon. "I wish you and Don the very best." Kati whirled around when Raul stepped up beside her.

"Are they getting married?" he asked.

Kati nodded, trying to hear his question and listen to her friend's joyous explanation of how the proposal came about. "He was worried about me being in the apartment alone," Jenny said. "He realized how much he loved me."

"I'm so pleased for you," Kati murmured.

"We're going to Connecticut to spend a week with his parents for our honeymoon. They have a cottage in the woods and we'll be staying there. Oh, isn't it wonderful?"

"Let me speak to her," Raul insisted, taking the phone from Kati's hand.

She started to speak sharply to him when she heard him say, "I want you and Don to come here to my home for your honeymoon." He paused and Kati knew Jenny was telling him she and Don already had plans. "I'm sorry that you can't come now," Raul responded, "but I insist that you come in the future. The invitation stands. Whenever you can come, you have only to call me. I'll send my private jet for you."

Kati raised stunned green eyes to his face, and she stared blankly at the telephone as he made several more comments, then handed it back to her. He had a private jet? He had a private jet, and would send it to pick up Jenny and Don, but he wouldn't send her home in it, knowing how badly she wanted to go!

Jenny was bubbling with excitement. "I'll be moving out of the apartment, of course. But I'll leave most of the furniture for you. Donny's apartment is decorated beautifully. Oh, do enjoy your vacation, Kati," she cried. "I'll see you when you get back."

"Of course, Jenny," Kati murmured. "Congratulations, again. Good-bye." Kati turned to Raul when she had replaced the phone. "If you have a private jet, why can't I fly home in it?"

Raul's manner was very calm in contrast to Kati's anger. "I don't want you to go home. I want you here with me. You agreed to stay and I'm not through showing you Mexico City. Are you ready to see the pyramids? It's not too hot today, and they are fascinating."

Kati felt like screaming at him, hitting out at him, hating him. "No!" she cried. "I'm through seeing the city with you! I honestly believed that you wanted me here to get to know your sick father, but I no longer believe that. I want to go home. How could you keep me here knowing that I want to go home so desperately?"

He reached out and gently cupped her chin with his hand. His dark ebony eyes probed deeply into her green ones. "Still, Kati?"

Her eyes met his. She knew he was alluding to last night, and she was ashamed that he had brought it up. "More than ever." Her gaze lowered under the bitter expression in his, and she felt his grip tighten on her chin momentarily before he released her. "Raul, I want a divorce," she muttered before she lost her nerve.

She regarded him with anxious eyes as she saw his lips tighten into a thin line. "I'll make the decision on a divorce," he growled between clenched teeth. With a smothered expletive, he turned away from her and strode angrily from the room.

Kati locked her fingers together and gripped them until they hurt. Why? Why was he keeping her here? It was plain that he no longer cared for her.

Upset and miserable, she made her way back out to the garden and sat down on the stone bench again. She was still there, staring unhappily at the cool water spurting from the fountain when Raul returned some time later. She glanced up at him apprehensively, and she was unable to miss the taut lines of his mouth. He glared at her for several moments, and she could see that he was undergoing some inner battle to remain composed. "Damn it, Kati," he snapped at last, "why do you have to be so damned impossible?"

"Me?" she cried. "You should take a look in the mirror."

"I don't want to argue with you today." He dismissed her with a wave of his hand. "I'm ready to go to the pyramids."

Incredulous, Kati glowered at him, finding it difficult to believe what he had said. "Well, good for you!" she retorted. "I don't want to go, and I won't go!"

He watched her for a moment, his eyes narrowed. "I don't care what you want," he replied coldly. "Get up and let's go."

Kati thought she must be hearing him incorrectly. Surely he wasn't demanding that she go. But yes, that was exactly what he was doing. He stood before her impatiently tapping his foot while she delayed. She drew a deep breath and let it slip through her lips. The man was simply unbelievable. "I give up!" she exclaimed angrily. "Take me any darned place you want! Do whatever you wish with me. My feelings have never mattered to you. You've *never* cared what I want." She stood up and started down the walkway. "Even when we lived together, you always did exactly what you wanted," she called over her shoulder. When she saw that Raul wasn't following her, she turned around to glare at him. "Are you coming, *master?*" she quipped sarcastically.

His eyes were pensive for a moment, and Kati wondered if she had finally impressed upon him her distaste for the way he was treating her. Suddenly, in four angry strides, he had reached her. Taking her by the shoulders, he shook her savagely. She gasped in shock at his fury, and she was breathless when he released her. Automatically, her arms crossed and she massaged the places where his fingers had bitten into her shoulders. "Now," he hissed, "tell me what you mean by that remark. What did I do with you when we lived as man and wife that you disapproved of? Either tell me now, and stop throwing it in my face, or forget it and *never* allude to it again."

Kati opened her mouth to speak. She wanted to tell him. She wanted to fling the sordid little story in his face at such close range. Just in time, she managed to control her pain and anger. No! She wouldn't give him the ultimate satisfaction of hearing it from her lips. He knew it, and he knew that she knew it. She shook her head determinedly, and looked at him with smoldering eyes. He would not make her admit that she had been a fool for him . . . and still was.

Chapter Eight

Taking her hand, he marched down the walkway and out to the car. Kati was powerless to do other than run along beside him, trying to keep up with his angry pace. As they drove along the highway, Kati was grateful that she was dressed in the gray slacks and comfortable silver top; it began to look like a good distance to the pyramids. She looked out at the scenery, finding it quite interesting. She and Raul didn't speak to each other as the miles sped away, and Kati tried to keep her mind on the rows of homes stacked on the hillsides and near the highway. Many of them were small and made of cement, with plots of land beside them growing corn and other vegetables. Clotheslines were strung from house to house, and dazzling white clothes fluttered from the lines.

They had traveled for some time in silence when Raul pointed to the right. "Look over there. You can see the pyramids."

Kati craned her slim neck, and she felt a little thrill at her first glimpse of them. She had intended to see them because, of course, she had heard of them and something about the mystery surrounding them. "I wonder why they were abandoned so suddenly," she mused.

It was the opening both of them needed to begin civil conversation and Raul answered her question with a slight shrug. "We can't know for sure, but it's speculated that the people who built those magnificent structures had much the same problem we're facing today.

Weather factors were undoubtedly involved, and perhaps there were changes in other areas which affected Teotihuacan's economy. This situation might have resulted in a shortage of raw materials for the specialized workshops which turned out export products such as knives and weapon heads. It is thought that they traded with other people in the area for cotton, jade, vermilion and large amounts of obsidian. Also, the increased number of carved military figures toward the end suggests that there may have been political or internal problems."

"It sounds absolutely fascinating," Kati said, excitement building inside her. "I never knew their civilization was so advanced, although, of course, everyone has heard of the Aztecs."

"These people weren't Aztecs," Raul said. "The Aztecs were the last ones to come to the valley. People are most familiar with them because they were the ones who were conquered by the Spaniards, but there were many other civilizations here before the Aztecs."

Kati was amazed by the information. "How interesting," she murmured.

"These pyramids are the oldest and the biggest in Mesoamerica. The first people who came to the valley came from the north, probably Asia. The pyramids were in ruins when the Aztecs came."

"Teo . . . Teotihuacan." Kati tried the name on her tongue, and it didn't fit well. "What does that mean?"

"The Aztecs named the city Teotihuacan, 'place where men become gods,' because they believed the city to be the cemetery for kings who became gods when they died. The Aztecs thought the pyramids had been built by giants because of their size. People lived in the city for about a thousand years before it was abandoned."

"How can you know?" she asked.

Raul shrugged again. "Of course we can't know any of the facts for certain, but scientists can now determine the age of artifacts, providing a reasonably reliable method of discovering details of history. We know, too, that the Aztecs settled in Mexico City, not in Teotihuacan."

"How many people lived in Teotihuacan?" Kati asked.

"Maybe as many as two hundred thousand when it was abandoned. It's still a mystery that has plagued historians as to why the city virtually disappeared."

"I wonder what the Spaniards thought about the pyramids," Kati said.

"The Spaniards never knew about them. Remember that the Aztecs built their city in what is now Mexico City where their priests found the eagle, snake and cactus. The pyramids had been abandoned for about seven hundred years when the Spaniards came, although it had continued to be a place of worship for Aztec pilgrims even after its abandonment. When the Spaniards conquered the Aztecs, the city was covered with vegetation. From a distance, it looked like the other mountains. The pyramids weren't officially discovered until 1905. Restoration and excavation are still going on. Of course the natives knew, but the city of Teotihuacan wasn't known in the rest of the world until the early nineteen hundreds."

"It's incredible!" Kati cried, her eyes searching the horizon for the pyramids. "How far is it now, Raul?" His information had captured her imagination, and she could almost see the inhabitants going about their business in the day-to-day life of hundreds of years ago.

"We're almost there, but you aren't really interested, are you, Kati?" he teased. "I had to force you to come with me."

She looked levelly at him, then lowered her eyes. He had forced her to come, but he knew she hadn't refused because of lack of desire to see the pyramids. The memory of last night and the way she had felt in his arms, giving herself to him with such abandon, burned in her mind, and she became silent again. Why did Raul insist on tormenting her with reminders? She felt badly enough about it as it was. She wanted to forget what she had done, how he had used her for his own pleasure. She remembered the abject misery she had felt as she sat by the water fountain with him before her.

Calling Jenny certainly hadn't helped. Of course she couldn't have told Jenny how miserable she was under the circumstances. Her own plight seemed even more tragic now that Jenny was going to marry the man of her dreams. Kati would spend her days alone in that lonely apartment.

"There," Raul commented. "To the right is the Pyramid of the Sun, and over there, to the left, is the Pyramid of the Moon."

Kati obediently followed his gaze, but she stared unseeingly at the nearing shapes, their magnificence paled now because of her preoccupation with her own monumental problems. Seeing Raul again had changed her life, a life she had worked so hard to rebuild after her short, devastating encounter with him ten months ago.

"Kati, we're here."

She glanced out the window; she hadn't realized Raul had turned down the long, dusty road to the parking area. Not waiting for him to open her door, she climbed out and looked around. She made up her mind that she would not let her unhappiness stand in the way of exploring the pyramids, and she let the aura of the ancient city fill her mind with awe.

"This way," Raul said. Kati moved up beside him, and they walked down a long row of stalls where vendors were selling the usual tourist souvenirs, as well as obsidian pieces the hawkers claimed to be from the area. Kati's eye was caught by a beautiful clay flute, sculptured with the bust of an Aztec in ceremonial headdress at the flared bottom of the instrument, and the head of an Aztec god done in glorious detail where the mouthpiece began. The colors were a cool green, remarkably like jade, a rich, earth brown and a soft beige. The young boy peddling the flute began to play a haunting, intriguing tune, his fingers moving skillfully over the openings of the instrument. Kati couldn't resist any longer. Tugging at Raul's hand, she said, "Please find out how much the flute costs, Raul."

Seeing that she was weakening, the seller tried to shove the flute into her hand. "How much do you want to pay, lady?" he asked in good English. "Here. Take it. It is yours."

Kati couldn't resist. She was fascinated with the colorful decorative instrument. She held it lovingly in her hand, willing to pay the boy whatever he wanted.

"If you don't like that one," he said, quickly pulling out several others from a pack on his back, "I have these."

"Oh, no!" Kati cried, wishing he hadn't told her about the others. She stared at the selection of other colors and other designs, all beautiful and enchanting. Now the choice would be impossible.

Misunderstanding her cry, the boy began to shove them back into his pack. "You take that one," he said with finality.

"Now I must examine the others," she insisted, rolling her eyes at Raul in mock exasperation. They were all so marvelous that she didn't know which one she wanted.

Puzzled by her behavior, the young seller dragged the others out again, four in all, knowing that he had a sure customer. He stated a price with conviction.

Raul scoffed at the price. Speaking quickly in Spanish, he soon had the amount reduced considerably. With Raul's help, Kati finally decided on one. They both laughed when they realized it was the one she had first been interested in. With the prize carefully stowed in her shoulder bag, she and Raul continued to the pyramids.

Raul took her hand, and Kati found herself momentarily distracted by his nearness. Determined not to let his touch dominate her, she allowed him to lead her down the dirt path to the first set of steps. Then she stood there at the site of the pyramids, gazing about in amazement. She had expected to see the two pyramids Raul had pointed out, and she knew a city had existed here, but she wasn't prepared to see so many pyramids laid out in such an orderly fashion.

"It's so large," she exclaimed.

"Yes. The city was eight square miles," he told her, helping her down the steep steps. "We can't cover it all because climbing the steps is enervating. First we will see the Temple of Quetzalcoatl. I want you to see the magnificent serpent heads and the detailed panels."

Following him silently, Kati tried to see everything at once. When they reached the temple, she cried, "Oh, Raul, how on earth did they make such an elaborate monument without the help of modern machinery?" She marveled at the huge, ornate stone head of a toothed serpent which seemed to come from the petals of a flower.

"Now you know why the Aztecs thought the pyramids were made by giants. Everything is done on a larger-than-life scale." He led her down a path along the sculptured walls of the temple. The day was warm and beautiful, and Kati marveled at the wonder of the pyramids against the grandeur of an azure sky.

"Where did they make the human sacrifices?" she asked. The thought sent a shiver up her sun-warmed body.

"You're thinking of the Aztecs and the Mayans," Raul replied. "It is believed that most of the sacrifices here were animal ones. The ceremonies were conducted on the platforms which were built to honor the gods." He pointed across the area in front of them. "There are many of them between the Pyramid of the Sun and the Pyramid of the Moon."

Kati stared from one pyramid to the other. Finally her eyes rested on the Pyramid of the Sun. She gazed at it in fascination. Hundreds of steps led up to different levels and there were people climbing up them. Some of the people were so far up that they looked like ants on the ledge at the top.

Raul smiled teasingly. "I don't think you can make it very far up the pyramid, Kati. The climb isn't an easy one, and I want you to be able to go to the ballet tonight."

Kati brightened in the face of the challenge, completely forgetting her intentions of being with Raul no more than she could help. In the splendor and the excitement of her surroundings, her brooding thoughts had vanished completely. "I can climb it, Raul, and I'd love to see the ballet. The travel agent said it's a must."

"But you said she hadn't seen Mexico," Raul teased.

Kati shrugged, too thrilled with the discoveries of the day to find his teasing annoying. "I believe her anyway. The tour guide also talked about it on Friday."

"It *is* a must," Raul said, squeezing her hand lightly. Kati pretended not to notice, but she couldn't suppress a warmth which flooded through her. "All right. Let's see how good a climber you are," Raul said.

Kati confidently strolled along beside him to the Pyramid of the Sun, all the while watching other people on the steps. Some made it to the top, seeming to crawl at a snail's pace; others gave up after the first few steps; and still others sat down to rest or to enjoy the astonishing view below. Kati was determined to be among those who made it to the top.

It didn't take her long to realize the folly of her ambition. The steps were narrow and incredibly steep and made of uneven stones. Besides, her breath seemed to be sucked away by the altitude. When she turned once to look down and chart her progress, she gasped at the dizzying height she had attained. The firmness of solid ground was so very far below. Inadvertently, she grasped Raul's hand tighter, and he slipped his arm around her waist. Once more she sucked in her breath, now fighting the dizzy sensation of his body so near hers as well as the formidable height of the pyramid.

"Let's turn back," Raul said. "You've gone far enough."

She stubbornly shook her head, although the idea was very appealing, and he was giving her a chance to back down. Her foot rose to climb one step and then another. She kept determinedly at her task, but it was just no use. She gazed up at the heavens and saw that the top of the pyramid loomed in front of her still some distance away. Ruefully, she was forced to admit defeat. Sinking down on a rocky step, she breathlessly admitted, "I can't go on, Raul. I'm exhausted." Shielding her eyes with her hand, she gazed up at the steps above her. "It's so far to the top," she murmured in disappointment.

Laughing, Raul sat down beside her. "It's sixty-five meters high," he said. "I was sure you couldn't climb it, but you gave it quite a try."

It irritated Kati that he wasn't even winded and that she had been forced to admit defeat. They were less than two-thirds of the way to the top, and others continued to pass them. Kati didn't want to look back down. She realized that heights weren't her strong point, and she longed to be safely on the ground without the necessity of treading her way back down the treacherous steps.

"You're a stubborn little thing," Raul murmured, his dark eyes searching her face, "hot-blooded and strong-willed like a Mexican, but physically you're like your Southern ancestors, Kati. You need to be pampered and looked after. You're a delicate flower with a flaming center to be nurtured and cared for."

"That's not true," she protested.

"Oh, but it is, Kati," he murmured knowingly. "It is. You just don't want to give in to the fact, but all that will change one day."

She frowned slightly, wondering exactly what meaning lay beneath his words, but he didn't elaborate, and she didn't pursue his statement. She drew a deep breath. "Well, I think we can start back now."

Raul rose to his feet and pulled Kati to hers to begin the descending trek. Kati felt as if she'd hiked miles and she plodded uncertainly along behind Raul, glad for his reassuring presence, her hand resting securely in his. Her foot slipped on the worn edges of the rocky path, and a small cry of alarm escaped her lips. Raul hugged her to his body, and the look in his eyes startled Kati.

"Are you all right?" he asked, his brows merging in a frown.

"I believe so," she managed to reply weakly. "I'll be glad when we're back down. The ancient civilizations can reclaim this pyramid. I've had enough of it." It was bad enough that she had been unable to reach the top; now she couldn't seem to reach the bottom without difficulty.

Raul released her, and Kati felt a sudden sense of loss when he stepped away from her. "Be careful where you step," he ordered firmly as they worked their way down. Kati glanced at him from beneath her lashes. His tone made it evident that he was annoyed with her, and she wished she hadn't needed to depend on him.

Kati was elated when they reached the bottom and she touched solid ground at last. Only when they had walked some distance from the pyramid could she look back at it with her original sense of awe. She liked it much better from a distance.

"Have you seen enough?" Raul asked. "Or do you want to explore the Pyramid of the Moon?"

"No, thank you," she replied, shaking her head firmly.

She was feeling quite drained and thirsty as they left the pyramids. Raul found a food stand and bought sandwiches and colas for their lunch. They strolled along slowly, Kati enjoying the cool, sweet, refreshing beverage and the tangy cheese sandwich. She thought of nothing but the moment and the magnificence of the city of Teotihuacan, now that she could view it objectively.

It wasn't until they were back in the car and Raul was talking about dinner and the ballet that she realized the day would soon be at an end. Would Raul think that he could coax her into his bed again? Would he even want to? She remembered how ashamed she had been this morning when she awakened, and she promised herself that she would not put herself in the position of feeling that way ever again.

Raul suggested that Kati take a nap before dinner, and she wasn't in the least reluctant. She was pleased about going to the ballet, and she did want to be refreshed enough to enjoy it. The trip to the pyramids had sapped her strength, and she had been foolish enough to let the prospect of Raul's behavior after the ballet upset her. She really must learn to live for the moment, she told herself. Just as Raul did. She would enjoy the evening and let the night take care of itself.

Going to the closet, she scanned her clothes for something appropriate to wear. She wished she had brought other dresses with her, but she hadn't anticipated attending several places which would require something special. Her eyes rested on the simple but stunning little black dress which had so pleased Darren the night she went to dinner with him. She knew it was sure to bring an unpleasant memory to Raul's mind, but then it reminded her that he had been with that girl. In a moment of rebellion, she pulled it from the hanger and put it on the bed. After all, twice Raul had paraded his women before her. The dress would be fitting for the ballet and she knew that it flattered her figure and coloring. Besides, she wasn't sure just how formal the attire should be, and the black dress would solve her problems. She went to the bathroom, filled the tub with warm water, and poured in bubble bath which had miraculously appeared in the room the day after she arrived. It was her favorite scent of magnolias, and she sniffed the fragrant air as she slipped into the warm water.

After fifteen heavenly minutes, she emerged and dressed. Lest the dress unduly upset Raul, she left her hair loose, cascading in a dark cloud over her shoulders the way he liked it. After applying her scant make-up, she slipped her feet into the backless, high black heels. She appraised her appearance in the full-length mirror, and she was pleased with it. Her cheeks were rosy from the day spent in the sun, and the little black dress had a magic all its own. Feeling confident, Kati went down to join Raul for dinner.

Her confidence waned in the face of his majestic appearance. Dressed in a cool, white linen sports jacket and formfitting black trousers, he was handsome—too handsome, she told herself. She fought down the impulse to run to him and wrap her arms around him, molding herself to the aristocratic length of him. He sat down on the couch, leaned back against the chair cushions and picked up the paper, unaware that Kati had come down the steps. She watched him for a moment, then crossed the room. When he heard her heels on the stone floor, he glanced up and caught her watching him. He smiled warmly, and Kati felt like a pat of butter left in the sun, melting under his deep, appreciative gaze.

"You look lovely, Kati," he murmured in a low voice, his eyes sweeping over her appreciatively. "Even if you did wear that dress for your American."

Kati was glad her sun-reddened cheeks concealed her blush. "Thank you, Raul," she said shyly, trying to drag up a measure of confidence. Darn! Why did he have to be so devastatingly attractive? She found herself thinking of his broad shoulders and his naked chest pressed against her breasts, his long legs intertwined with hers. She looked away quickly, afraid that he could read the desire in her eyes.

She didn't see him rise and walk toward her. When she heard his steps on the floor, it was too late. His hand found her long hair and fanned through the midnight strands. Before Kati had time to protest, Raul's lips lowered to hers and kissed her sweetly.

"Don't, Raul," she murmured when he raised his head. "Don't do that."

"Why not?" he asked. "Are you going to tell me that you don't like it?"

"I don't!" she insisted, raising her chin defiantly as she turned away from him.

Raul laughed lightly, then cupped her face to force her eyes to meet his. Holding her chin securely, he traced her lips with a teasing fingertip. "Your lips say no, but your eyes say yes."

"They don't," she said firmly, brushing his hand away and stepping back out of his reach. She was relieved that he hadn't mentioned last night and the way she had given herself to him so eagerly. She didn't want the subject to come up. "Is dinner ready?" she asked. "I'm starving. The walk today really made me hungry."

"Oh?" he asked. Kati was sure his tone was mocking. "Well, then, we must see if Hortencia is ready to serve us." His eyes moved down her figure again. "I wouldn't want you to lose an ounce of weight, *querida.*" He studied her figure carefully, causing a heat to rise in her face.

Flustered, Kati turned away again, and she was angered when Raul chuckled softly. Without waiting for him, she walked toward the dining room.

Hortencia, beaming as always, looked at both of them when they entered the room. She was adjusting the place settings. "I'm glad you are here," she said. "Dinner is ready. I hope you are very hungry for I have prepared the master's favorite."

Kati looked at Raul, and she was amazed that he accepted Hortencia's term for him, apparently as his just due. She glanced back at the cook, finding it incredible that anyone in this day and age would refer to someone as master, but Hortencia was busy with her work, obviously not caring what direction Kati's thoughts took.

Raul pulled out a chair for Kati, and she sat down across from him at the long table. She had become used to its size and she thought nothing of the two of them sitting there. Only when she looked down at her place setting did she realize that there was a third place set at the table. She looked up at Raul.

"Father is joining us for dinner tonight," he said simply, and Kati was surprised at the wary look in his eyes. She looked away as Hortencia came bustling back in with a fancy-looking dish of food and set it before Raul. It smelled wonderful.

"It's *ternera en nogada,*" Raul said. "Veal in walnut sauce."

Kati gazed at the dish expectantly, but she was surprised when Hortencia served her. She had thought they would wait for Señor Torres.

"Taste it," Raul urged. "Then tell me if Hortencia isn't the very best cook in all of Mexico."

Picking up her fork, Kati sampled the dish. "Mmmm," she readily conceded, "it's heavenly." The thin strips of meat were tender and delicious, and the sauce was rich and tantalizing.

Hortencia stood by, her hands folded in front of her, and again Kati saw the two gold teeth as the woman smiled broadly. "I'm pleased that you like it, señora. I serve it often since it is Señor Raul's favorite, and it would be a shame if you didn't like it."

Kati colored at the implication in Hortencia's statement. Of course the servants didn't realize that she was only here for two weeks, then would vanish as quickly as she had come, taking only her clothes and her bittersweet memories of her husband and his city with her.

"Thank you," she mumbled. She took another bite, and she was grateful when Hortencia disappeared and she was able to concentrate on her dinner. She and Raul ate in silence for several minutes, both of them

lost in thought as they savored the delectable dish.
"Shouldn't we wait for your father?" Kati asked uncomfortably.

Raul's eyes met hers as his fork paused in midair. "Father knows what time dinner is served."

Kati was about to reply when the older Señor Torres entered the room. Raul stood up immediately. "Good evening, Father. We're delighted that you can join us for dinner."

Kati looked in the man's direction, offering him a weak smile. He didn't seem too happy to join them, and she wasn't at all sure she was delighted that he had. "Good evening," she murmured politely.

He nodded curtly, and Kati wondered if the man were ever going to speak to her at all. Sitting down before the place setting which had been set next to Kati, he placed his napkin on his lap without a word, and served himself.

"How are you feeling, Father?" Raul asked as he sat back down.

Señor Torres gazed at him sullenly. "All right, I guess."

"Good," Raul said. "Kati and I are going to the ballet *folklorico* and we would like to have you join us."

"I don't think I feel that well," he retorted immediately.

"Nonsense, Father," Raul replied lightly. "Where are your manners? Do you want Kati to think you don't wish to spend any time with her?"

Señor Torres's dark eyes raked over his son's face, and Kati saw an almost imperceptible twitch of his lips. "Why would she think that, Raul?" he asked. "I have been ill."

Kati was chilled by his tone. She was beginning to think that he really *didn't* want to spend any time with her. What on earth was Raul trying to do to her? Why had he insisted upon her getting to know his father?

"The ballet will be good for you," Raul said. It was

plain that he was gently pressuring his father, and Kati hated him for it. She had been so looking forward to the ballet; now she didn't want to go at all. The evening was becoming less appealing with each passing minute.

Raul resumed eating, and Kati and Señor Torres followed his example. "Do you know anything about the ballet *folklorico?*" he asked.

Kati shook her head, her eyes meeting his. "Only that the guide said the ballet company is considered one of the best in the world."

"You can say that about anything in Mexico," Raul said with a grin. "Including me."

Kati didn't comment, and Raul laughed. "But anyway, the ballet company is one of the best. One woman is responsible for the greatness of the troupe. She is a former dancer who studied classical and modern ballet, then found herself drawn to the songs and dances of her own country. She explored the riches of Mexico and formed a company of her own. She no longer dances, but under her guidance and direction, the company has toured many countries, and of course here in Mexico, our people flock to it. It's held tonight in the Fine Arts Palace, a most beautiful and impressive building. I'm sure you will enjoy the evening."

"Yes," Kati murmured. "I think so."

"I *promise* you will," Raul emphasized, and Kati's eyes lowered at the gleam in his. He was talking about the ballet, wasn't he? She returned to her meal with renewed interest, glad that it kept her occupied.

Dinner passed with remarkable swiftness even though the conversation was awkward with Señor Torres contributing very little. The three of them were lingering over coffee and dessert when there was a commotion at the front door. Kati experienced a sinking sensation when Raul stood up with a broad smile on his lips.

"Good. You're back," he exclaimed, moving away from the table as someone came into the room.

Kati looked over her shoulder to see who it was, and

her breath caught in her throat. Brisa had sauntered into the room, and Kati sat still, mortified as Raul embraced the tall girl. Brisa tilted her face to look up into his. Right before Kati's eyes, she placed a lingering kiss on his lips! Kati felt a seething jealousy and outrage rise inside her. How dare he drag her here to his house and then have his mistress appear? She was snapped out of her black thoughts as she watched Brisa walk over to Raul's father, kiss him on the lips, and murmur something softly in Spanish before she turned to Kati.

"How are you, Kati?" she purred in a slightly accented, sugary voice.

Kati forced her eyes to meet Brisa's brilliant ones. They were a very deep brown with strange yellow accents, vivid and bright against a background of shimmering hair the same dark brown. Involuntarily, Kati's eyes wandered to the girl's tall, lean figure. She was very lovely, Kati conceded miserably. Her jealousy flared anew. "How are you, Brisa?" she asked dully. Only her shock and embarrassment at finding herself in such a position kept her in her chair before the enemy.

"I'm fine, as you can see," the other girl replied.

Kati looked at Raul, wishing the look had the power to kill. How could he do this to her?

"Won't you join us for coffee?" he asked, ignoring Kati's mutinous glare. "We've just finished dinner, and we're soon off to the ballet. You must join us, of course."

"Of course you must, pet," Señor Torres added, and Kati turned to stare at him. His weathered old face had brightened as if by magic, and his sullen tone had evaporated. He *was* unhappy at being coerced into spending time with her, for it was blatantly obvious that his condition improved instantly when Brisa, whom he obviously adored, appeared.

"Kati." Raul's voice prodded her to attention. "Do you want more coffee?"

She glanced at him quickly, hating him for what he had done to her, and for the situation she found herself in now. If only she could get up from her chair and escape, she would do so. She definitely had no intention of staying in Raul's home now with Brisa here. She felt tears rise to her eyes. How could Raul do such a thing? Did he despise her so much? She bit down on her lower lip, unable to meet the eyes of the others as Hortencia bustled about with a cup and fresh coffee.

"More coffee, Kati?" Raul repeated.

Ruefully, she lifted her chin and shook her head. "No. No more for me."

"Are you enjoying our home, Kati?" Brisa asked as she settled into the chair next to Raul.

Kati looked at the other girl. Our home, she mused. Was Brisa talking about the house or the city? She locked her fingers together and swallowed hard. "It's beautiful," she replied ambiguously. Surely Brisa didn't live here when she was in the city. She just couldn't!

"Which room did Raul put you in?"

Kati choked on the question. She was forced to take a sip of water before she could reply. "The yellow one at the top of the stairs."

"Ahh, that one. It was Morganna's."

Kati stared at her blankly, not knowing who Morganna was, and not caring.

"My mother," Raul clarified.

Kati didn't know what to say, so she nodded.

"And it hasn't been used since she left," Señor Torres added tartly, looking pointedly at Raul.

"Then it's time it got some use, don't you think?" Raul asked, giving the older man a half-smile.

Señor Torres lifted his coffee cup to take a long sip. When he set it back down, he pretended to study its contents. Kati couldn't help but think that the man seemed to despise her, and she was terribly uncomfortable. He fell silent while Brisa chattered to Raul about the import-export business and the weather. Kati was surprised to hear Brisa say that she would miss all of the hustle-bustle and the confusion now that she was quitting work, but she didn't dare ask why the girl was quitting. She was afraid to know the answer.

Abruptly, Raul stood up. "We don't want to be late for the ballet. Not only do I not want to miss any of the performance, but I detest latecomers crawling over me, and I don't want to be guilty of it myself. Let's get started."

Kati looked at him, marveling that he was so considerate of complete strangers' feelings, yet he subjected her to more abuse than she could tolerate. Did he really imagine that she would go to the ballet now, regardless of how much she wanted to see it and had anticipated the pleasure? He stepped around behind her chair and slid it back. Kati walked with him as far as the living room, and forcing a smile, she proudly lifted her chin and turned to Brisa and Señor Torres who followed.

"Brisa," she said with a cool nod of her head. "Señor Torres. Good evening." Her eyes strayed to Raul's face. "I have a terrible headache, and I won't be going after all. I'm sure the three of you will enjoy yourselves."

Glancing at Señor Torres, she was unable to miss the curious look in his eyes. Had he thought her a stupid little creature, too simple to realize that he disliked her, and too uncaring to object to Brisa's appearance? Her head held high, she walked to the stairs, and she marched rigidly to her room without a backward look.

Chapter Nine

Kati was aware that Raul was behind her, but she acknowledged him neither verbally nor with her attention. When she reached her door, she felt herself jerked around sharply.

Dark threatening eyes glared down into hers. "You won't embarrass me in front of my father, and you *will* go to the ballet, so you just march yourself right back down those stairs. I don't care what you tell the others, but you will go. Your headache can vanish as quickly as it came."

"Let me go!" she hissed, her green eyes brilliant with anger. "I wouldn't go to heaven with you and . . . and Brisa if you were Saint Peter and she were an angel sent to lead the way! Or with your father!" she added for good measure. "You're not blind. Don't you care that your father has behaved rudely to me? Why, he has barely acknowledged my presence, but the minute Brisa came into the room, he made a miraculous recovery! Oh, Raul," she cried suddenly, a tremor in her voice, "why are you doing this? Haven't you inflicted enough pain on me?"

His eyes blazed as angrily as hers had when they raked over her face and down her taut figure. "And what pain have *I* inflicted on *you, querida?*" he asked softly, but she didn't miss the menace in his tone.

She lowered her eyes, unwilling to give him the satisfaction of hearing her repeat his escapades with Brisa and the other women.

"Tell me, Kati," he ordered in a low, demanding voice.

She raised glistening green eyes to the moody darkness of his. "You know, Raul," she murmured.

"Do I? Tell me and let's see."

"I don't think there's room for both me and Brisa in your home or your heart, Raul," she said sadly.

His brows arched up in surprise. "Brisa again," he muttered. "I've tried to explain to you that we grew up together. She has often been a guest in my home. My father adores her."

"And you don't?" Kati asked mockingly, her lips quivering as she gave voice to the painful question. She jumped when she heard someone behind them.

"Raul, we're going to be late," Brisa complained petulantly. "If Kati has a headache, let her lie down. Your father's waiting."

Raul looked over his shoulder at the tall beauty. "Coming, Brisa." He grasped Kati's wrist firmly. "Kati feels well enough to come with us."

Without giving her further chance to protest, he pulled her along the hallway and down the steps. She wouldn't give either of them the satisfaction of seeing her make a scene. Mustering all the dignity she had, she held herself regally and struggled along beside Raul, trying to keep up with his long strides. And she hated him more than ever. She had known that he was cruel and insensitive, but to subject her to an evening with his . . . his mistress and his father was intolerable and inexcusable.

José drove them to the ballet, Raul and Kati sitting in front, and Señor Torres and Brisa in back. Brisa continued to chatter brightly and confidently, and Kati was only too well aware that Señor Torres responded interestedly to her comments. Raul remained quiet as did Kati.

"You're so quiet," Brisa said too sweetly as they neared the Fine Arts Palace. "Perhaps you should let

José drive you back home, Kati. We'll get along without you."

Kati looked at Raul. He was watching her, but he offered no retort to Brisa's comment. She seethed with anger, and she determined that she wouldn't let Brisa have her way if it was the last thing she did. Looking back over her shoulder, she smiled coolly. "I'm sure you would, but I don't think Raul could. He wanted me to come so badly that he practically dragged me. I wouldn't dream of missing the performance now that we're here. Besides, I feel quite all right now. But thank you. You're *so* kind to be concerned." The smile died on her lips as she turned back to the front, but she didn't miss the amused look on Raul's face. Let him smirk, Kati thought. She had had it with Brisa's sarcasm.

When José stopped in front of the Palace, Raul helped Kati out, but she refused his arm. Brisa was escorted by Señor Torres, and though she clung to his arm, her eyes followed Raul.

When they were seated, Brisa had managed to sit between the two men while Kati sat on Raul's right, but she didn't care. She wanted to be as far away from the girl and Raul's father as she could possibly be. She wouldn't be here at all if she had been given any choice.

They had been seated only a few minutes when the lights were dimmed and the music began. As the dancers began to make their entrance, Kati became so gradually engrossed in the magic that she almost succeeded in suppressing her anger. Young men dressed in brief, colorful Aztec costumes, complete with tall, golden feathered headdresses, did four dances, exploring man's relationship with the gods. The movements were enchanting and well executed, and Kati watched intently, lost in the mood of a primitive and exotic Mexico of long ago. Only when the dances ended, and the crowd clapped enthusiastically, did she confront her circumstances. Her hand accidentally brushed Raul's arm, but she looked straight ahead, pretending nothing had happened.

Kati loved the varied and beautiful costumes of the next group of dancers as they spun and whirled to a lively tune. The women wore great flounced skirts, small black flowered aprons, white blouses and thin, triangular shawls secured at the bosom by simple brooches. Their heads were adorned with flowers of brilliant red, colorful bows and decorative combs. The men were dressed in white, long-sleeved shirts, white trousers, red kerchiefs tied around their necks, cowboy hats and tall boots with taps.

Moved by the gay music Kati tried desperately to concentrate on the ballet; it was much too marvelous not to enjoy. Pretending that she was there alone, she tried to lose herself in the mood and the wonder as the dancers took her back to a more simple Mexico. She adored the wedding dance, and she was delighted by the sugar harvest dance, but her imagination was captured most completely by the revolution dance in which Mexican women joined the men in their political struggle in 1910. Kati loved the folk songs and the sight of the women marching in their colorful costumes with mock rifles. When the curtain descended for intermission, Kati stood up and clapped loudly with the rest of the audience. She tried to ignore Raul standing beside her, watching her.

"Did you enjoy it?" he asked.

"Yes," she replied tersely. "Excuse me, please."

Raul stepped back against his seat so that Kati could pass by him, and he seemed not to notice that her body brushed his. Kati was acutely aware of it. How could she possibly find his touch exciting when his mistress stood by his side? Summoning all the hate in her, she moved past Brisa and Señor Torres without a word, but when she reached the aisle, she saw that Brisa had followed her. Not looking back, Kati rushed forward.

Brisa confronted her when they reached the door marked DAMAS. "Why have you come back?" she demanded without preliminaries. "Why didn't you stay in North Carolina? You must know that your marriage to Raul is over."

Of course Kati knew it, but she wouldn't concede that to Brisa. "Is it?" she asked. "Perhaps you should tell him. It wasn't my idea to stay in his home." She looked down at her nails, pretending to study them. "I suppose he found that he didn't want you after all, Brisa."

But Brisa was much better at the game than Kati. "Do you *really* suppose that?" she asked with a mocking laugh. "Or do you suppose that he wants to show you Mexico City as he promised, then be rid of you once and for all? It's funny, isn't it?" she asked, "what some men think is important. Raul has often told me that he promised you a tour of the city."

"Yes," Kati murmured, "it is funny what some men think is important." She felt her insides quiver. Was that all Raul had wanted?

"By the way," Brisa said indifferently, "thanks for designing my wedding gown. It's beautiful."

Kati gasped. Raul and Brisa were going to be married! Of course she had considered the possibility that Raul would marry the girl, but to hear Brisa confirm her suspicions hurt more than she had imagined possible. Even though she tried to remain composed, desperately attempting to hide her pain, she felt the color drain from her face. "I didn't design your wedding gown," she hissed. She looked away when a woman brushed past her to enter the restroom, and her heart began to pound dangerously as she stood before Brisa. Reluctantly, she dragged her eyes to the other girl's again.

"But you did," Brisa said sweetly. "If you don't believe me, look in my closet. My room is the third one down from yours, same side. Raul bought your sketch, and he was very pleased with the way the dress looked when it was made up." Giving Kati a taunting smile, Brisa turned on a shapely leg and walked away.

Kati shoved against the bathroom door with a shaking hand. She didn't know if her legs would function well enough to carry her inside. Had Brisa been telling the truth? Kati hadn't designed a wedding gown, but several of her party dresses would have served nicely as a wedding dress. Her mind skimmed quickly down the many sketches she had done, then lingered on the four she had sold: one which she had a copy of in green her boss, Mr. Harris, had manufactured; another looked very much like the one that singer, Carmela Castillo, was wearing; the third she had briefly imagined the pretty señorita by Raul's side at dinner was wearing; and the fourth was a waltz-length, flounce-sleeved, scalloped-necked gown with a fitted waist. A sick feeling settled in her stomach. Was it possible? Could it be? The last one would have made a beautiful gown; she had suggested that herself to Mr. Martin when she had worked briefly for him in New York, but he hadn't wanted to mass-produce the dress. She had sold all four to Mr. Harris in the past seven months since she had left Raul.

Kati was sure Raul knew where she worked in North Carolina, but would he have bought her sketches? She was very much afraid to know the answer. Drawing a deep breath, she went to a couch and sat down until the lights flickered signaling the resumption of the performance. She was appalled by the possibility that Raul might have bought her sketches for his lady friends. Could even *he* subject her to such an indignity? And Brisa's wedding gown! The injustice of Raul purchasing a sketch for his future bride was an almost unbearable agony.

Aware that the three members of her party were watching her, Kati slipped past them and silently took her seat beside Raul. She wanted to demand that he tell her if he was the one who had bought the sketches, but she didn't want to cause a scene during the performance. Raul had obviously already made the decision to divorce her since Brisa had made wedding plans.

Keeping her eyes glued to the curtain in front of her, Kati stared straight ahead. She didn't breathe normally until the curtain rose and the dancers began to come to life on the vast stage.

The performance was exceptional, but no amount of concentration would keep Kati's mind on the dancers. She was too shocked and sickened by Brisa's revelation. Could it really be that Raul had bought her dress designs for his mistresses? For Brisa? For their wedding? She simply couldn't believe it. Her mind refused to accept such cruelty. Even Raul wouldn't do such a thing. Would he?

All the dancers merged like the swirling colors of the gala dresses they wore. Only one dance stood out for Kati as the ballet came to an end. A dark young man with a beautiful body covered by only a brief fawn-colored costume and a deer headdress danced slowly and sensually to the music of drums and a reed flute. As he danced, he shook the rattles he held in both hands, tossing his head back in a proud gesture.

Kati was entranced by his dance, and a shiver ran up her spine when the deer looked up and all around. His body tensed as he sensed danger. Two hunters jumped out before him, menacing in their very appearance. For a short time, the deer evaded them, but eventually he was felled by an arrow. Kati watched unhappily as he staggered to his death, fell to the earth and struggled desperately to live as a single drum sounded his final heartbeats. At last he lay still: his dance was over. The curtain descended, and Kati found that she had tears in her eyes, so moved had she been by his proud beauty and his struggle against death. A black curtain dropped, obscuring him from sight.

When the curtain rose again, it was to the gaiety and frivolity of towering figures with huge make-believe heads who danced out in the aisles, throwing colorful streamers and confetti to children and adults alike. Raul caught a string of red and handed it to Kati. She accepted it without a word; she didn't need a souvenir of this night. She would never be able to forget it as it was.

The dancers returned to the stage amid resounding applause, and the curtain dropped a final time. The spectators began to disperse, and Raul's hand reached for Kati's. Unwillingly, she let him guide her out of the theater and down to the car where José waited for them. Brisa and Señor Torres climbed in first, and no one spoke as Kati and Raul got into the front for the ride back to the house.

They arrived home very late. Kati's first thought was to grab her suitcase and demand that José drive her to a hotel, but pride made her want to stay and face Raul and Brisa this time. She was suddenly weary of running away. She had to know the situation here so that she could go on with her life when she went back to the States. And she had to see for herself if Raul had actually bought her dress design for Brisa. She and Raul weren't even divorced yet, though that was obviously a mere formality at this stage. But to think that he would hand her the ultimate insult of buying her design for Brisa's gown . . . it was unbelievable!

Too tired and emotionally drained to do other than retire, Kati pleaded the headache again, this time in earnest. She was thankful that Raul didn't protest or bother to walk with her up to her room. But then why should he? Brisa was here now. With a stiff good night, she left the room. From the corner of her eye, she saw Raul sit down on the couch with Brisa and his father.

Slipping out of the black dress, Kati let it fall carelessly to the floor. She took a nightgown from the massive chest of drawers and pulled it over her head. Then she collapsed on top of the bed covers. She couldn't understand Raul's insensitivity, and she could only conclude that he was punishing her. But to take her one last dream, her designing, and flaunt it in her face so savagely! And if he loved Brisa, why had he made love to her last night? Was it only to prove that she was still in love with him? Did it soothe his male ego to know that she hadn't left him because she had stopped caring for him? She remembered that he had said that first night he intended to prove that she loved him. All right. He had accomplished that. Perhaps he would let her go now.

She laughed aloud bitterly. She had stayed out of his arms for seven months, only to give in to him five days after seeing him again. Now they were right back where they had been seven months ago. He was with Brisa and Kati was feeling abused and heartsick. She had fallen right back into his arms as though nothing had gone wrong between them. She knew it would take her years to get over the heartache of her Mexican vacation, and she had come expecting to have a good time! Rolling over on her stomach, she smothered her face in her pillow and sobbed long into the night. But there was no one to care. She could barely hear the sound of the others talking down below. They weren't even aware that she was in the house.

The next morning, Kati donned a pale blue sleeveless, high-necked dress and low-heeled navy shoes. When she went down to breakfast, she found only the cook in the dining room. For once Hortencia wasn't smiling. She looked up at Kati solemnly. "Good morning," she said. "What do you want for breakfast?"

Looking at her watch, Kati saw that it was only eight o'clock. "Have the others eaten?" she asked.

"The Señores Torres have eaten," the cook replied. "Miss Mendoza doesn't eat breakfast. She has had fresh coffee in her room. Three cups of coffee," Hortencia added. "Each from a fresh pot."

"I see," Kati murmured. She could just imagine Brisa lying in bed, summoning the cook three times for a cup of coffee. "If there's any left over, I'd like a cup, please, and toast."

Kati watched the cook walk away, and she was a little relieved that she wasn't the only one who found Brisa unpleasant. Brisa and the wedding dress. Kati couldn't bear to think about it on an empty stomach, but she made up her mind that she would go to Brisa's room and see for herself if the woman's wedding gown had been made from Kati's design. She realized ruefully that she couldn't convince herself that Raul would do such a rotten thing as to buy his next wife a gown Kati had designed. Funny, she mused absently, she had never thought he cared for her designs.

Sitting down at the table, she waited for Hortencia to return with the coffee and toast. She smiled at the woman when she came through the archway. Hortencia's good humor seemed somewhat revived, and she smiled back as she set Kati's breakfast down. Fresh butter and apricot jam were on a dish with the toast, but Kati ate without too much enthusiasm.

After she had finished, she stoically walked up the stairs to the third room down from hers. She tapped lightly and waited with barely trembling knees for some response from Brisa. It had occurred to her that she might find Raul inside with Brisa, but she closed her mind to the possibility.

"*Adelante,*" Brisa called out sweetly. Kati opened the door to find the tall beauty lying on the bed in her pajamas, reading a glamor magazine.

"Oh, it's you," she remarked, sitting up and crossing her long legs in front of her. "What can I do for you?" A knowing gleam shone in her yellow brown eyes. "Do you want to see my wedding dress?"

"Yes," Kati replied with some effort.

Brisa got up and trailed barefoot to the closet. Kati was surprised to find herself praying that the gown wouldn't be her design, but she was destined to have her prayer go unanswered. Brisa slid the other dresses aside, slipped a garment bag off one, and there it was! Kati had designed that dress eight months ago, and while Mr. Harris didn't feel that it would sell well enough to warrant mass production, he was interested in the design. He had promised Kati to show it to some of his more influential and wealthy customers, and to take it to nationwide meetings with him. When he had phoned Kati to tell her he had an interested party willing to purchase it for an original dress, she had been thrilled and had readily agreed. She had been surprised that the dress hadn't been made at the factory, but then Mr. Harris seldom did any originals. Kati smiled bitterly: someone had made a few insignificant alterations in her sketch; the neckline was lower than what she had intended, and the waist was more pronounced, but it was her design all right. And Raul had bought it for Brisa. She remembered what Paco had said about her wedding dress at the fashion show, and she wondered if the dress had been made at his factory.

"Well?" Brisa prompted.

"It's lovely," Kati remarked through tight lips. "I don't often have a chance to see my designs done up. I don't sell many, you see." She looked levelly at Brisa and hoped her broken heart wasn't reflected in the misty green of her eyes. "The field is very competitive and this is only the fourth design I've sold."

"Oh, you might sell others," Brisa replied offhandedly. "I shall have Raul show me what you've done from time to time . . . perhaps. And I think Carmela Castillo is interested in your work."

Kati forced a tight smile. "Yes. I saw her in one of my designs night before last." She really hadn't been sure that it was her design, and she hoped Brisa would confirm or deny her suspicions. "It looked beautiful on her."

Brisa's smile was oddly crooked. "Raul told you about the dress?"

Kati shrugged nonchalantly. "He took me to see the singer." She could read nothing in the sly smile that stretched Brisa's lips, and she dared not stay longer in the woman's room. Her heart was pounding savagely and she felt short of breath. Raul had been the one to buy two of her originals . . . perhaps three. And it was apparent now that he had done it maliciously. Otherwise, why would he make sure that she knew he had bought them for his other women?

"I'm sure you'll look lovely in the gown," Kati managed to say. She touched the garment bag. "At least the bag is sturdy," she added more evenly than she had imagined possible. "I'm afraid you'll need to keep the gown covered for some time. Your groom isn't quite ready for marriage, is he?"

Brisa frowned slightly. "Hasn't Raul told you about the wedding?"

Kati swallowed hard. "All that I want to hear about the wedding, I've found out. My experience with weddings hasn't been pleasant, but obviously you think you'll fare better than I did."

"I see," Brisa replied.

Kati backed out of the closet, then turned on her heel and marched stiffly toward the door. Tears were forming in her eyes, but she would rather die before she let the other girl see them.

"Kati."

Automatically, Kati whirled around at the sound of her name. Brisa was watching her with a curious expression on her face.

"You really do love Raul, don't you?" she asked.

Why should Kati bother to deny it? It was written all over her face. "Yes," she said bitterly. "I really do. Isn't that a laugh?" Then she turned on her heel and fled from the room. She could almost feel Brisa smiling smugly as she shut the door behind her. As she stumbled down the hall to her room, she felt a sob rise in her throat. How could Raul have done it? How could he? Did he take some perverse pleasure in it? He had chosen her design when he could have selected one from a thousand established, well-known designers. He certainly had the money to pay their prices. Why had he used her little design? It wasn't even that unique. Had he intended for her to know about the gown?

She managed to retreat to her room and throw herself down on the bed. Then, although she fought against the spilling of bitter tears, they streamed down her cheeks. Raul had inserted the knife in her broken heart and twisted it cruelly. All she had left was her dress designing and her dreams of making something of her career, and now she couldn't even derive satisfaction from that. Raul had made a mockery of her ambition. He had been the one to buy her three designs which she had hoped would give her some recognition. She didn't hear the knock on her door, or the steps toward her bed. She looked up at Raul in surprise, tears clouding her vision.

"Kati," he murmured consolingly, "what's wrong?" Sitting down on the edge of the bed, he tried to pull her into his arms, but Kati freed herself and slapped him across the face. The move caught him unaware, and he pulled back in surprise, glaring at her as the red rushed to his dark cheek, forming the imprint of her hand.

"Why, Raul?" she cried angrily. "Why did you do it? Do you despise me so much that you make a mockery of my dress designs?"

"What are you talking about?" he demanded coldly.

Kati sat up against the headboard, wrapping her arms around her legs and sniffling. "I'm talking about Brisa's wedding dress!" she sobbed.

"What about it?"

"What about it?" she cried. "How dare you buy my design for her wedding dress? How dare you? Who do you think you are to treat me that way? I hate you! I hate you! Do you hear me? I don't want to stay here another hour. Let me go to a hotel!"

Raul stood up slowly, staring down at her all the while. "I didn't know Brisa was going to show you the dress yet, Kati," he said in a low, dangerous tone. "I had intended to tell you later."

"And what did you think I would do then?" she demanded harshly. "Cry for joy because you had bought my design?"

Kati watched as Raul stood before her angrily clenching and unclenching his fists, his jaw muscle working savagely. Suddenly his hand shot out and he gripped a handful of her long, dark hair. "I thought you would be pleased that Brisa would be wearing your gown," he said in an icy, clipped voice. "But then I've never known what would give you pleasure. Perhaps a divorce will." Releasing her, he shoved her back on the bed.

Kati watched, barely breathing, heart beating wildly, as, tall and erect, Raul left the room. "Pleased," she cried when her voice could be found. "Pleased!" Either the man was a fool or colder than even she had surmised. Huddling into a small ball, she hugged her legs as the tears began to trickle down her cheeks again.

Kati didn't know how she finally managed to fall asleep, or how long she had slept, but she was awakened by a gentle tapping on her door. "Who is it?" she asked, rolling over on her side and running a hand through her damp, matted hair. God, she must look a fright.

"Hortencia."

Kati sat up. "Come in."

"Señor Torres wants you down for lunch," the cook said, her smile wavering in the face of Kati's dishevelled, distraught appearance.

"Tell him to go jump in a lake," Kati muttered.

Hortencia stood staring at her uncertainly.

"Well," Kati insisted, "tell him!"

A deep frown marred the smooth brown lines of Hortencia's face. She shrugged one shoulder and turned away, vanishing out the door.

"The master has sent an order to one of his harem," Kati told herself sourly. She hoped he choked on his lunch. Scooting to the edge of the bed, she got up on shaky legs to go to the bathroom. After slipping out of her dress, she secured her hair on top of her head, turned on the shower water, stepped out of her undergarments and into the tub. For a couple of minutes, she let the warm water beat down on her face and body. Reaching for a bar of soap, she lathered all over. She had just stepped under the spray to rinse off when the taps were abruptly turned off and the shower curtain ripped back.

"What are you doing?" Kati yelped, seeing Raul standing before her. She tried to cover herself with her hands, but it was a futile attempt.

"The next time you have a message for me, bring it yourself," he said coldly. "Now get dressed and get downstairs for lunch."

"I won't!" she cried.

"You will if I have to drag you!" he announced.

"You wouldn't!"

But she knew by the look in his eyes that he would.

"Try me," he challenged coolly.

"Why?" she screamed at him. "What are you trying to prove?"

His eyes flicked insolently over her before he replied. "I told you that when you asked me on Thursday. I intended to prove that you love me."

"All right!" she flared. "All right! You've proved it! Do you want to rub it in? Now let me leave this house. Take me to a hotel. I don't want to stay here with you, Brisa and your father. I don't give a hoot what the three of you do, but don't include me. Go eat lunch with Brisa."

Raul's eyes searched Kati's face and she was surprised by the disconcerting look she saw there. "Did I prove that you love me, Kati?" he asked in a strangely soft voice. "The knowledge came at such a high cost that I hardly realized I'd gotten you to admit it. Even your admission has been a cold and empty victory to me." His eyes wandered over her soapy curves. "But under no circumstances will I take you back to the hotel. You agreed to stay the duration of your vacation and get to know my father. When will you stop running away? Can't you see any commitment to the end . . . even a two-week vacation?"

"Oh, Raul," she pleaded suddenly, looking at him with hurt, confused eyes, "don't subject me to this. I know as much about your father as I want to know . . . more, and it's plain that he dislikes me."

For a moment she was sure she saw compassion in his eyes. Perhaps he was through tormenting her. Perhaps he had extracted his peculiar kind of justice. But her hope was short-lived. He was unrelenting. "Come down and have lunch."

Kati stared at him with stricken eyes. "This is hardly my idea of a vacation," she cried. "I don't want to share my time with the three of you. I could have seen my own plans to the end, but not yours and Jenny's!" It didn't matter that Jenny had thought she was doing the best thing for Kati. Her motive didn't count. She had sent Kati into the lion's mouth, and the lion wasn't through with her yet.

Suddenly Raul reached out and touched her exposed breasts. "The soap is drying," he said gently. "Finish your bath." Then he bent down and turned the taps back on, closing the shower curtain as he moved away.

For a long time Kati stood immobile with the warm spray pounding down on her. Raul had no heart at all. It was hard to believe that she had ever rested in his arms peacefully in the dark hours of the night. He was a cruel, insensitive monster. Maybe he would even invite her to the wedding, she thought despairingly. And he would probably expect her to go!

Finally forcing movement, she rinsed off the remains of the soap and reached out for a gold towel. When she had dried off, she brushed her hair, letting it cascade freely down her back. She told herself that it was because it was very damp, but she knew she did it to call Raul's attention to it. Slipping into her red dress, she stared at the forlorn creature she saw in the mirror. Her heartache was caught in her green eyes for all to see, and she wondered if the others would find it as obvious as she did. She had admitted to Raul that she still loved him. She had given herself to him. He had bought her designs and dressed his mistresses. How much more could he possibly demand of her?

Chapter Ten

Kati swallowed nervously as she entered the dining room. The others glanced up when she appeared, and Kati watched as Raul stood up and pulled out a chair for her near his. She would rather have sat down at the very end, away from the three of them, but she didn't want a scene with Raul. She had already learned that invariably she was the loser in the battle, and Brisa had done enough gloating at her expense.

Kati looked at Señor Torres and saw that he was staring at her intently. The air was tension-filled, and suddenly Kati wondered what the three of them had been discussing while they waited for her. Hortencia came in as soon as Kati was seated, and Kati realized that she had been waiting to serve them. Any other time, she would have apologized for keeping the others waiting, but she said nothing as her gaze again met Señor Torres'. She saw a tight smile play on his lips, but she didn't return it. She had no idea why he bothered to force the faint smile at this point when they both knew he didn't care for her. Kati watched as the two men exchanged a meaningful glance.

Señor Torres' gaze fell on her again. "You look unwell," he said in a tired voice. He sighed, and he appeared to be struggling to speak civilly. "I hope I haven't caused you undue discomfort by my rudeness." His eyes again met Raul's before they returned to Kati. "My son seems to think I owe you an apology."

Kati wiggled uncomfortably in her chair, not knowing how to respond. She looked away from his hard gaze and saw that Brisa was watching her with a peculiar look on her face.

"I must tell you frankly," Señor Torres continued in a monotone, "that I didn't want Raul to marry an American, and I was relieved when I thought the marriage had ended as quickly as it began. I had hoped that he would marry a Mexican woman. He has disappointed me terribly."

A small blaze of anger became full-blown inside Kati when Señor Torres dismissed her with his eyes and picked up his wine glass. "Then we have at least something in common, Mr. . . . Señor Torres," she amended. "Raul has disappointed me terribly, also, but you've no need to explain your position to me. I wouldn't be here at all if Raul hadn't demanded that I stay to get to know you." She moistened her quivering lips with her tongue. "It was a dreadful mistake. And," she added, tears filling her eyes, "I am relieved that the marriage is over, too. I see all too plainly now that it was impossible, considering Raul's background. The time I've spent here has opened my eyes to a lot of things."

A deadly silence fell over the room as Señor Torres stared wide-eyed at Raul, then back at Kati. "What do you mean?"

She blinked back her tears and drew a deep breath to try to still her pounding heart. "Please don't insult me further by pretending that you don't know," she replied. "It occurs to me that you and your son have used me to revenge yourselves against an American woman who hurt you." She watched his dark eyes grow even darker. "I'm sure you know that Raul's behavior toward me has been intolerable."

A grim look flickered over Raul's lips as he met his father's eyes. That put them both in their places, Kati told herself unhappily. Now that they both knew where they stood with her, she dismissed the subject as casually as Señor Torres had done, but she didn't think her stomach would ever stop somersaulting.

"Pass the salt, please," she requested with an incredibly calm voice when Hortencia set a crisp salad down before her. She had as much pride in her country and her race as anyone, and she wouldn't have them condescend to her again. And she certainly wouldn't take the blame for her failed marriage. She wouldn't be treated abominably because of Morganna Torres and the scars she had left. Kati glanced up, refusing to let any of them see how she was trembling.

Making a wry face, Brisa picked up the salt shaker and passed it to Kati. Kati hoped the other girl couldn't see how her fingers shook when she accepted it.

Somehow Kati endured the lunch, then excused herself to return to her room. She spent some time sketching, trying to keep her mind off her unhappiness, but she couldn't create a single design. She kept seeing Brisa's gown and her eyes filled with tears, causing her vision to be too blurred for her to work. When she could stand it no longer, she hurried down the stairs and out onto the patio. For a long time she sat before the water fountain, lost in thought. She realized ruefully that she hoped Raul would come to her, but when some time had passed, she listlessly returned to her room. She didn't realize that hours had elapsed until she heard the rap on her door. It was Hortencia again.

"Dinner will be served at six," the cook announced coolly when Kati answered. Apparently she was annoyed about the last message which she had been made to deliver to Raul.

Kati offered her a conciliatory smile. "Hortencia, I'm not very hungry. Is it possible for someone to bring me a glass of milk later?"

"I'll see," she said, closing the door before Kati could speak again.

Some time later, Guadalupe appeared with the milk, and Kati gladly took it. She didn't want to think about why Raul was agreeing to her absence from dinner. She hadn't needed to hear him make the comment about a divorce, for she knew that it was inevitable anyway if he were marrying Brisa. But that didn't stop a bitterness from surfacing at the thought. Had Raul wanted to be sure that he was finished with Kati before he made the final commitment to Brisa? Why had he told her he loved her when he made love to her? She shook her head. What did it all matter now?

Again she tried to sketch, but she couldn't concentrate. Not wanting to join the others, she whiled away the hours until bedtime. Tomorrow she would demand that Raul call the airline and get her on a standby flight. There was no point in continuing this farce of a vacation. She lay down on the bed, a picture of Raul in her mind. She had almost dozed off, despite the image, when she heard a sharp rap on her door.

Kati's eyes opened wide when she answered the knock and found Señor Torres in the hall. "I would like to come in," he said, his manner curt.

She stepped aside so that he could enter. His eyes dull, his stance belligerent, he said without any preliminaries, "Let me be brief, señora. If I have wronged you, I apologize, but I am an old man, as you can see. I loved one American, and she almost destroyed me. I put my hopes and dreams in the hands of my only son, and he betrayed me by doing the one thing sure to hurt me: he, too, married an American, against my wishes. And now it seems that I must abandon my plans for a grandson. My blood will never run in the veins of another Torres man. Yes, I am bitter, but I don't want to accuse you unduly."

Kati blinked as she stood before the man. Why should his dreams of a grandson not come true? Surely he was getting what he hoped for with the marriage between Brisa and Raul. Before she could think of any reply, Señor Torres had gone from her room. Kati stood watching the door close, clenching her hands until her nails bit into her palms. Accuse her unduly, indeed! "Damn!" she cried angrily. Why hadn't she told him about Raul's betrayal of her? Why should he be the only one to think he had been wronged!

Miserable, she stripped off her dress and changed into her nightgown. Picking up her sketch pad again, she climbed into bed, but she was too unhappy to sketch or sleep. She lay awake long into the morning hours.

When Kati finally woke up the next day, it was well after ten o'clock. Determined to leave Raul's house, she marched downstairs, prepared to face the lions like a Christian going into the arena. She was surprised to see three suitcases lined against the living room wall, near the door. Someone was obviously going away. She glanced up as Guadalupe walked into the room. "Where is Raul?" she asked.

"I'll get him for you, señora," the housekeeper said as she hurried away.

Kati stood waiting impatiently for him to appear and it was only minutes later when he stepped into the room.

"Good morning, Kati," he said.

"Raul, I . . ."

He held up a silencing hand. "Please pack, then have your breakfast. I've arranged for my jet to take you back to North Carolina."

For a single minute, Kati stared at him in surprise. She didn't know why the information should shock her. She swallowed hard, and an ironic smile played on her lips. She hadn't even had the chance to tell him that she insisted on leaving today; he wanted her to go. He wanted to be free to pursue his plans with Brisa. Inexplicably, tears rose to her eyes, and she blinked them back, not understanding why she should feel so hurt. This was what she wanted, what she had known had to happen.

"Fine," she whispered, not bothering to tell him that it had been her intention to leave anyway. She watched as he turned and strode away. Her tears began to trickle down her face as she made her way back to her room.

She packed quickly, leaving her suitcase unlocked in case she should need to put in any last-minute item she had forgotten. When she went to the dining room, she found that Hortencia had already prepared eggs and fruit for her breakfast, but she barely picked at the food: her stomach was somersaulting, and she was only a blink away from tears. She shoved her plate aside. Now that Raul had decided to be rid of her, she was being tossed out like yesterday's newspaper. Returning to the living room, she found that Raul, Brisa and Señor Torres were waiting for her, as well as her packed suitcase. "I'll just go and get my purse," she murmured, unable to meet the eyes of the others. Apparently they were all going away as well as she. No wonder Raul was in a hurry to be rid of her.

She picked up her shoulder bag and rushed back downstairs. If she had left anything behind, it would have to remain behind.

There was a general air of excitement in the car as José drove them to the airport. Brisa was chattering gaily about nothing and everything, and the two men were subdued but pleasant. Kati couldn't have spoken if she had tried. There was a big lump in her throat, and she was terrified that she would cry at any moment. Confusion, shame and disappointment all churned within her.

Upon their arrival at the airport, Raul escorted Kati to his private plane while José helped a baggage boy load the others' luggage on a baggage cart. Kati looked back over her shoulder to see Brisa and Señor Torres staring after her and Raul, and she was embarrassed by her speedy dismissal.

Raul introduced Kati to his pilot, and she was grateful to see that he was an American. After Raul had handed her suitcase to the pilot, he turned to face Kati. Her eyes valiantly met his, and she fought back tears as she watched him stand rigidly before her. "Kati," he said, his eyes dark and unreadable as he grasped her chin firmly in one hand. Their eyes locked briefly, then he gave her chin a little jerk and released her. "Have a pleasant trip back to North Carolina," he said curtly. Then abruptly, he turned and strode away from her.

A single tear slipped from Kati's eye and trickled down her flushed cheeks. So, it was finally over—her Mexican vacation—and her marriage to Raul Torres.

"Are you ready, miss?"

Without a word, Kati climbed aboard the plane and found a seat.

Kati took a taxi from the airport to her apartment. With her luggage in hand, she trailed forlornly up the steps to the quiet, lonely apartment and went inside. The apartment seemed empty and unfamiliar without Jenny in it. She had taken many of her belongings, but had left the basics for Kati. Kati wandered about the familiar rooms feeling lost. Finally she lifted her suitcase onto the bed and opened it. As she began to unpack and hang her clothes, she was amazed to realize how much room the small closet had when it was empty of Jenny's clothes.

When she reached for the last blouse, she was surprised to find the three paintings Raul had left on the bed for her the morning after she had made love with him. He must have slipped the paintings in when he went up to get her suitcase while she ate breakfast. But why had he done it? To torment her further? She sat down on the bed and gazed unhappily at the gaily colored works. She had been so pleased when they had selected them, but now they were mute reminders of Raul and her disastrous Mexican vacation. And she didn't need any physical reminders. Her mind was flooded with mental ones. Every time she thought of Mexico, she thought of Raul, and the most painful memory of all was her hand striking his handsome face. It was even more painful than seeing Brisa's wedding gown. She let the paintings fall to the floor and went to hang her blouse. She would forget. She had to forget or go crazy.

On Monday morning Kati went back to work. She still had vacation time left, but she didn't know what to do with herself. She couldn't mope around the apartment forever; she needed to keep busy. Jenny was still away, and even if she were home, Kati couldn't spoil her happiness by telling her what had happened in Mexico.

The moment she was inside the factory, she confronted Mr. Harris about the sketches he had sold to Raul, but he insisted that he hadn't known who bought them, only that the interested party was willing to pay well for them, and that the buyer was familiar with Kati's work. Kati felt guilty when she saw the exasperated look on her boss's face; he couldn't help the fact that Raul had bought them. He had done Kati a favor by showing her designs.

"Did I do something wrong?" he asked. "I thought you were pleased."

A blush crept up Kati's face. "I was pleased," she murmured. "Of course you didn't do anything wrong. I . . . I was flattered that someone bought them."

"How was your vacation?" he asked.

"Fine," she replied absently.

"Then why did you return so soon?"

"It was much too warm there," she said, using the first excuse that came to mind even if it wasn't quite true. "Much too warm for me." The response was her salvation as the day wore on. She was asked the same two questions over and over until she wearied of them.

Kati was relieved when the days began to pass, and the topic of her vacation ceased to be of interest. Life settled down at work and at home. She became used to being in the little apartment alone, and she reconciled herself to the prospect of spending a lifetime alone.

Jenny was happily married, and Kati expected news of her impending divorce from Raul any day. She was sure now that he would get one of those quick divorces the rich seemed to be able to procure; it was just a matter of time.

When a letter arrived from Mexico, she wasn't surprised. The contents, however, took her breath away. She pulled out a wedding picture and announcement and stared wide-eyed at the picture of the beautiful Brisa in the gown Kati had designed. Brisa was lovely, and the gown was exquisite. Kati's fingers trembled as she tried to read the clipping. It was in Spanish, and she wondered if this were more of Raul's cruelty. She saw the name Torres, but not Raul. It was possible that she didn't know what she was looking for, but could Brisa and Raul have married already? Perhaps the clipping was an engagement announcement, but the gown was clearly the one Brisa had said she would wear to her wedding. Had they married as soon as Kati left? Was it conceivable?

Snatching up her purse, she hurried to her car and drove to the local library. She knew the librarian, Mrs. Reva, could read Spanish. Breathlessly, she rushed into the library to Mrs. Reva's desk.

"Excuse me, but can you interpret this for me, please?"

Mrs. Reva smiled patiently, and with the slowness of a snail, she took the clipping from Kati's trembling hand and read it to herself. "Well, yes," she said at last. "It's a wedding announcement. Do you want me to read it to you?"

"Yes," Kati sighed, feeling her heart sink.

"It reads: Señor Javier Torres, cousin of Señorita Brisa Mendoza, is happy to announce her marriage to Señor Carlos Arreguin in Acapulco. Señor Arreguin is in the oil business, and the new Señora Arreguin is a former employee of the Torres import-export firm in New York City."

Mrs. Reva looked up when Kati gasped softly. Kati

reached for the clipping but Mrs. Reva asked, "Don't you want to hear the rest of it?"

Kati nodded dumbly. What more could there be? Raul hadn't married Brisa and that was all that mattered.

"Señora Arreguin's wedding gown is an original done in satin and lace, and designed by the wife of the cousin of the bride, Señora Kati Autumn Torres, who also designs dresses for Carmela Castillo."

Kati blinked her green eyes twice; she wanted to ask Mrs. Reva to read that part again, but she didn't want to impose on the woman any longer. Again she held out a trembling hand, and clutching the clipping to her breast, she stumbled back out to her car. Why hadn't Raul told her? Had he wanted to drive her mad? And Brisa—she hadn't said that she was marrying Raul, but she had deliberately left out any mention of her fiancé. Kati thought back over the conversation, every word of it etched into her mind, and she wondered if Brisa had intentionally left the impression that she was marrying Raul.

Tears filled her eyes as she started her car. Had she been wrong all along? The clipping had confirmed that Brisa was Raul's cousin as he had contended. Had there been nothing more between Raul and Brisa than family affection? No, it couldn't have been only that. Kati was sure that Brisa cared deeply for Raul. And Raul had taken Brisa with him to Mexico City that Christmas last year. And he hadn't called her that night. A flush traveled up the length of her body. Was it possible that she was wrong? Had she blown things out of proportion with just a few hints from Brisa? Did Raul have some logical explanation for taking Brisa with him and for not returning Kati's call? It was true that Raul had flirted outrageously with other women, and he had teased Kati unmercifully, but she wouldn't have ended her marriage for those reasons. She loved Raul too much, and she knew a man like him would always be appealing to pretty women.

Feeling an aching emptiness deep inside, she parked her car and walked up the steps to her apartment. Raul had tried so hard to make things right again between them in Mexico City. And she had done everything in her power to make him despise her. And she had succeeded!

She gasped as she reached her front door and looked up into Raul's handsome face. He was leaning against the door, his legs crossed below the knees. "Hello, Kati," he said casually, but his black eyes glowed feverishly. "I see you got my calling card." His gaze shifted to the clipping still clutched in Kati's hand. "Do you need an interpreter, or have you read it?"

"Oh, Raul," she murmured, "I thought . . . I thought you bought the wedding gown design for Brisa."

"I did," he said.

"I mean," Kati whispered, "I mean I thought you meant to make her your bride."

"I have the bride I want," he said in a low, husky voice. "If only I can make her understand that. Can't we go inside where we can talk in comfort?"

"Yes. Yes, of course." Kati was so nervous that Raul had to help her with the lock. She ran a shaking hand through her hair as she invited him to sit on the sofa. Standing before him, she waited for him to speak.

"Sit down," he said soothingly, patting a place on the sofa beside him. When Kati had complied, he spoke again. "The wedding gown was the one thing Brisa wanted from me. I gave it to her as a wedding gift. She had seen your designs at the penthouse." He smiled wryly. "In return, she gave me something the day of her wedding. She told me that you had called that Christmas Eve last year when I went to Mexico City. Brisa arrived a short time after I did. She didn't bother to tell me that you had called because, like my father, she felt that you were no good for me." He smiled faintly. "And perhaps, too, because she cared a little more for me than she should have. She couldn't have known that you would run away, however. After all this time, she told me you had called because she really believes that you love me and that you can make me happy. Do you believe that, Kati?" he asked softly.

Kati laughed and the sound echoed faintly of hysteria. "You didn't take Brisa to Mexico with you?"

He shook his head. "I have explained to you that Brisa is my cousin . . . second cousin, actually, and I confess that my father wanted very badly for me to marry her, but that was never my intention. When I met you, Kati, my whole life changed." He shrugged carelessly. "It's true that you may not have known that, but I wanted to settle down suddenly. I wanted to return to Mexico City and live quietly there with you and have children. But you made it plain to me that your career was of primary importance."

"Why didn't you tell me how you felt about Mexico City and children instead of demanding that I give up my career, Raul?" she asked, her green eyes pained. "And why didn't you take me to Mexico City with you?"

"I am a man," he said simply. "I wanted you to put my desires before all else. I didn't see why I should have to do other than ask you to quit designing. As for taking you to Mexico City . . . well, you have met my father. You know how badly he wanted me to marry a Mexican girl and give him a grandson. He was terribly embittered by my mother's desertion. He never forgave her, and he blamed all Americans." His dark eyes held Kati's. "I knew how upset he would be when I told him I had married an American, and I didn't want to alienate him by giving him the news over the phone. He's an old man, Kati, and you may not understand this, but Mexican families are very close. There is a special closeness between a son and his father. Besides," he added softly, "I couldn't bear to have him hurt your feelings. That's why I wanted to explain things to him before he met you. And look what resulted. Christmas night I phoned the penthouse until I was half-crazy, but you weren't there. The cook said you had packed your belongings and gone away. I didn't know why you had run away the first day I had left you alone. I flew back to New York, but I couldn't find you for days. I was frantic with worry."

Kati reached out and took his lean hand in hers. "Oh, Raul, I'm so sorry. I thought you were having an affair with Brisa. You flirted with her so much, and I could tell that she cared for you."

"I am sure she would have married me if I had ever proposed," he conceded. "I have a real affection for her, but not the way you think, *querida*. I have never met any other woman I wanted for my bride but you."

"But why did you buy my dress designs, Raul? How did you know I was still sketching? Mr. Harris doesn't hire designers."

Raul smiled gently. "I really do think that you have talent, Kati. I was much too jealous of the time your career might take from me to admit it, but I knew that you could be famous with the right break. I have kept up with all you've done through phone calls to Jenny. When I told you the first night in Mexico City that jealousy was the culprit in our marriage, I didn't mean only your jealousy, but mine, too, over anything that would take you from me. At first I was sure you loved me and would return to me, but as time wore on, I really began to wonder if I had been a fool for you. I had too much pride to beg you to come back to me. I was afraid there was another man involved."

"Another man!" she cried. "Why would you think that?"

"You returned to North Carolina," he said. "You left New York where you had a better chance of earning your way as a designer. And Jenny did mention a Henry Bowden."

"Henry is an old friend," she explained quietly. "There has been no man but you, Raul."

A small smile played on his lips. "I thought not," he murmured, "but I didn't want to be blind to the possibility that you could find another man attractive."

"Who is the singer?" Kati asked, looking evenly at him.

"Carmela is an old, old friend of mine. I knew that the glamorous dresses you designed would be beautiful on an entertainer, so I asked Joe Martin to send for your designs. Then I chose one for Carmela and I bought the one Brisa had admired in New York. I had hoped to lure you back by showing you that I wanted anything for you that would make you happy. I have never stopped loving you, Kati. I called Jenny often to see how you were, and I made her promise not to tell you."

"Oh, Raul," Kati cried, *"I've* never stopped loving *you.* I've dreamed a thousand times that you would come to me and explain away all the hurt."

He gathered her in his arms and crushed her to him. "Kati, these past months have been hell for me. I've wanted to come to you a thousand times, but I didn't know why you had run away, and I wouldn't let myself chase after you. I thought I could win you again if only I could make you understand me, and I could show you how much I love you. That's why your plans for a vacation played right into my hands . . . or so I thought. When I saw you in Mexico City that first night, I was determined to make you my wife again if I had to force you to stay with me. That's why I insisted that you see the sights and meet my father. I was sure I could make you see that though we had had some misunderstandings, our love for each other was strong. I failed. You were just as determined not to understand me or my city. I knew I had only two weeks to convince you, and I went about it the wrong way. You're too stubborn to be forced to do anything."

"Oh, Raul, I did want to stay with you, but my pride had been hurt so badly. And it seemed that you were trying to throw your women in my face. Who was that pretty señorita at dinner with you that night?"

"Another cousin," he declared with a wry smile. "If you had been in your hotel that night, Kati, things might have been different. The girl, Maria, is Brisa's sister, and she, too, was wearing one of your designs. Didn't you notice? It was the surprise I had for you. I wanted to show you that I wanted you so much I was willing to do anything in my power to make you happy . . . even promote your career. When I saw you with that American, I wanted to break his neck. I promised myself then that I wouldn't bribe you with the gowns to make you stay. I wanted to force you to tell me that you loved me to convince myself that you truly did. But I couldn't believe that you didn't recognize that gown or Carmela's as your design."

"I was suspicious," Kati murmured softly. "But it seemed to be too much of a coincidence. Besides, I was too hurt to think rationally. I thought both women were your mistresses."

"You're my only mistress," he said in a husky voice. "Come back home with me to Mexico City. You will love it there. I'm sure of it. And I did accomplish something keeping you there. My father has great respect for you. In time he will come to love you as much as I do, but even that is not important. We will start again, *querida,* and this time you will not run away from me. You can open a fashion house if that's your desire." He laughed lightly. "You will be a great success. I have already assured that with Brisa's wedding announcement . . . as well as documented my relationship with her in black and white so that you can see she is no threat to you."

A shy smile trembled on her lips. "Right now, I'd rather make a grandson for your father than make dresses," she admitted, her brilliant green eyes hidden beneath lowered dark lashes.

"Oh, *querida,*" he groaned, tilting her head so that

she was forced to look into his eyes, "you can do both. Just never leave me again."

A sigh escaped Kati's softly parted lips as Raul's descended to claim them. Her arms stole around his neck and she pulled him more closely to her. She knew that wild horses wouldn't be able to drag her away from him again. She forgot all about her months of misery as he lifted her in his arms and carried her to the bedroom. This time she knew a thousand dreams were going to come true for her. And a thousand, thousand more.

Silhouette Romance